A. Grunbaum

ABOUT

VECTORS

D1214304

As far as the laws of mathematics
refer to reality, they are not certain;
and as far as they are certain,
they do not refer to reality.

ALBERT EINSTEIN

Adolf Grunbaum

BANESH HOFFMANN

Professor of Mathematics
Queens College of the City University of New York

ABOUT VECTORS

PRENTICE-HALL, INC.

Englewood Cliffs, New Jersey

PRENTICE-HALL MATHEMATICS SERIES

©1966 by
Prentice-Hall, Inc., Englewood Cliffs, N. J.

All rights reserved.
No part of this book may be reproduced in any form,
by mimeograph or any other means,
without permission in writing from the publisher.

Current Printing (last digit):
10 9 8 7 6 5 4 3 2 1

Library of Congress Catalog Card Number: 66-12118
Printed in the United States of America
C00076

PRENTICE-HALL INTERNATIONAL, INC., *London*
PRENTICE-HALL OF AUSTRALIA, PTY. LTD., *Sydney*
PRENTICE-HALL OF CANADA, LTD., *Toronto*
PRENTICE-HALL OF INDIA (PRIVATE) LTD., *New Delhi*
PRENTICE-HALL OF JAPAN, INC., *Tokyo*

PREFACE

This book is written as much to disturb and annoy as to instruct. Indeed, it seeks to instruct primarily by being disturbing and annoying, and it is often deliberately provocative. If it should cause heated discussion and a re-examination of fundamentals in classroom and mathematics club it will have achieved one of its main purposes.

It is intended as a supplement and corrective to textbooks, and as collateral reading in all courses that deal with vectors. Because the exercises call for no great manipulative skill, and the book avoids using the calculus, it may at first sight seem to be elementary. But it is not. It has something for the beginner, to be sure. But it also has something for quite advanced students—and something, too, for their instructors.

I have tried to face awkward questions rather than achieve a spurious simplicity by sweeping them under the rug. To counteract the impression that axioms and definitions are easily come by and that mathematics is a thing of frozen beauty rather than something imperfect and growing, I have mixed pure and applied mathematics and have made the problem of defining vectors a developing, unresolved *leitmotif*. The book is unconventional, and to describe it further here would be to blunt its intended effect by giving away too much of the plot. A brief word of warning will not be amiss, however. There are no pat answers in this book. I often present ideas in conventional form only to show later that they need modification because of unexpected difficulties, my aim being to induce a healthy skepticism. But too much healthy skepticism can be decidedly unhealthy. The reader should therefore realize that the ideas could have been presented far more hearteningly as a sequence of ever-deepening insights and, thus, of successive mathematical triumphs rather than defeats. If he reads between the lines he will see that, in a significant sense, they are indeed so presented.

To my friends Professors Arthur B. Brown and Václav Hlavatý, who read the manuscript, go my warmest thanks. It is impossible to express the depth of my indebtedness to them for their penetrating comments, which have led to major improvements in the text. They should not be held accountable for the views expressed in the book: on some issues I resisted the urgent advice of one or the other of them. A ground-breaking book of this sort is unlikely to be free of debatable views and outright errors, and for all of these I bear the sole responsibility.

BANESH HOFFMANN

CONTENTS

1

INTRODUCING VECTORS

1. DEFINING A VECTOR

Making good definitions is not easy. The story goes that when the philosopher Plato defined *Man* as "a two-legged animal without feathers," Diogenes produced a plucked cock and said "Here is Plato's man." Because of this, the definition was patched up by adding the phrase "and having broad nails"; and there, unfortunately, the story ends. But what if Diogenes had countered by presenting Plato with the feathers he had plucked?

Exercise 1.1 What? [Note that Plato would now have feathers.]

Exercise 1.2 Under what circumstances could an elephant qualify as a man according to the above definition?

A *vector* is often defined as *an entity having both magnitude and direction.* But that is not a good definition. For example, an arrow-headed line segment like this

has both magnitude (its length) and direction, and it is often used as a drawing of a vector; yet it is not a vector. Nor is an archer's arrow a vector, though it, too, has both magnitude and direction.

To define a vector we have to add to the above definition something analogous to "and having broad nails," and even then we shall find ourselves not wholly satisfied with the definition. But it will let us start, and we can try patching up the definition further as we proceed—and we may even find ourselves replacing it by a quite different sort of definition later on. If, in the end, we have the uneasy feeling that we have still not found a completely satisfactory definition of a vector, we need not be dismayed, for it is the nature of definitions not to be completely satisfactory, and we shall have learned pretty well what a vector is anyway, just as we know, without being able to give a satisfactory definition, what a man is—well enough to be able to criticize Plato's definition.

Exercise 1.3 Define a *door.*

Exercise 1.4 Pick holes in your definition of a *door.*

Exercise 1.5 According to your definition, is a movable partition between two rooms a door?

2. THE PARALLELOGRAM LAW

The main thing we have to add to the magnitude-and-direction definition of a vector is the following:

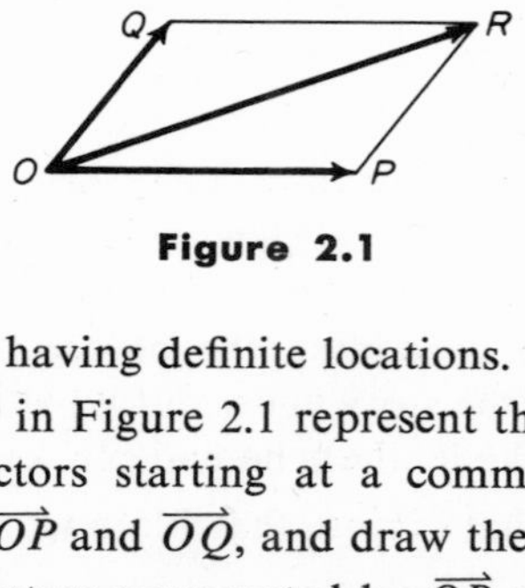

Figure 2.1

Let us think of vectors as having definite locations. And let the arrow-headed line segments $\overrightarrow{OP}$ and $\overrightarrow{OQ}$ in Figure 2.1 represent the magnitudes, directions, and locations of two vectors starting at a common point O. Complete the parallelogram formed by $\overrightarrow{OP}$ and $\overrightarrow{OQ}$, and draw the diagonal OR. Then, when taken together, the two vectors represented by $\overrightarrow{OP}$ and $\overrightarrow{OQ}$ are equivalent to a single vector represented by the arrow-headed line segment $\overrightarrow{OR}$. This vector is called the *resultant* of the vectors represented by $\overrightarrow{OP}$ and $\overrightarrow{OQ}$, and the above crucial property of vectors is called the *parallelogram law* of combination of vectors.

Exercise 2.1 Find (a) by drawing and measurement, and (b) by calculation using Pythagoras' theorem, the magnitude and direction of the resultant of two vectors $\overrightarrow{OP}$ and $\overrightarrow{OQ}$ if each has magnitude 3, and $\overrightarrow{OP}$ points thus $\longrightarrow$ while $\overrightarrow{OQ}$ points perpendicularly, thus $\uparrow$. [*Ans.* The magnitude is $3\sqrt{2}$, or approximately 4.2, and the direction bisects the right angle between $\overrightarrow{OP}$ and $\overrightarrow{OQ}$.]

Exercise 2.2 Show that the resultant of two vectors $\overrightarrow{OP}$ and $\overrightarrow{OQ}$ that point in the same direction is a vector pointing in the same direction and having a magnitude equal to the sum of the magnitudes of $\overrightarrow{OP}$ and $\overrightarrow{OQ}$. [Imagine the parallelogram in Figure 2.1 squashed flat into a line.]

Exercise 2.3 Taking a hint from Exercise 2.2, describe the resultant of two vectors $\overrightarrow{OP}$ and $\overrightarrow{OQ}$ that point in opposite directions.

Exercise 2.4 In Exercise 2.3, what would be the resultant if $\overrightarrow{OP}$ and $\overrightarrow{OQ}$ had equal magnitudes? [Do you notice anything queer when you compare this resultant vector with the definition of a vector?]

Exercise 2.5 Observe that the resultant of $\overrightarrow{OP}$ and $\overrightarrow{OQ}$ is the same as the resultant of $\overrightarrow{OQ}$ and $\overrightarrow{OP}$. [This is trivially obvious, but keep it in mind nevertheless. We shall return to it later.]

In practice, all we need to draw is half the parallelogram in Figure 2.1—either triangle OPR or triangle OQR. When we do this it looks as if we had combined two vectors $\overrightarrow{OP}$ and $\overrightarrow{PR}$ (or $\overrightarrow{OQ}$ and $\overrightarrow{QR}$) end-to-end like this, even

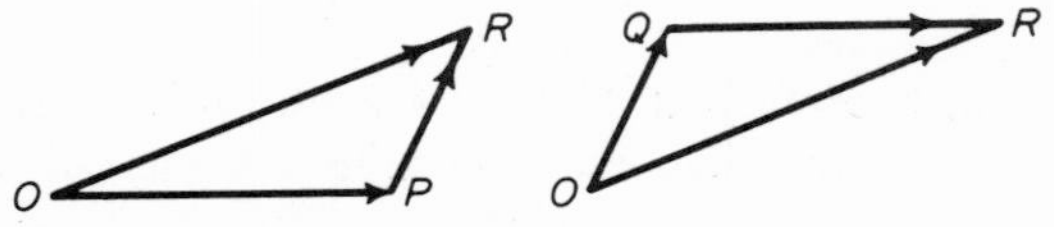

Figure 2.2 (For clarity, the arrow heads meeting at R have been slightly displaced. We shall occasionally displace other arrow heads under similar circumstances.)

though they do not have the same starting point. Actually, though, we have merely combined $\overrightarrow{OP}$ and $\overrightarrow{OQ}$ by the parallelogram law.* But suppose we were dealing with what are called *free vectors*—vectors having the freedom to move from one location to another, so that $\overrightarrow{OP}$ and $\overrightarrow{QR}$ in Figure 2.2, for example, which have the same magnitude and the same direction, are officially counted not as distinct vectors but as the same free vector. Then we could indeed combine free vectors that were quite far apart by bringing them end-to-end, like $\overrightarrow{OP}$ and $\overrightarrow{PR}$ in Figure 2.2. But since we could also combine them according to the parallelogram law by moving them so that they have a common starting point, like $\overrightarrow{OP}$ and $\overrightarrow{OQ}$ in Figure 2.1, the parallelogram law is the basic one. Note that when we speak of the same direction we mean just that, and not opposite directions—north and south are not the same direction.

*Have you noticed that we have been careless in sometimes speaking of "the vector represented by $\overrightarrow{OP}$," at other times calling it simply "the vector $\overrightarrow{OP}$," and now calling it just "$\overrightarrow{OP}$"? This is deliberate—and standard practice among mathematicians. Using meticulous wording is sometimes too much of an effort once the crucial point has been made.

Exercise 2.6 Find the resultant of the three vectors $\overrightarrow{OA}$, $\overrightarrow{OB}$, and $\overrightarrow{OC}$ in the diagram.

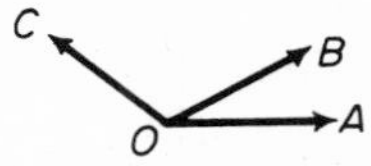

Solution We first form the resultant, $\overrightarrow{OR}$, of $\overrightarrow{OA}$ and $\overrightarrow{OB}$ like this:

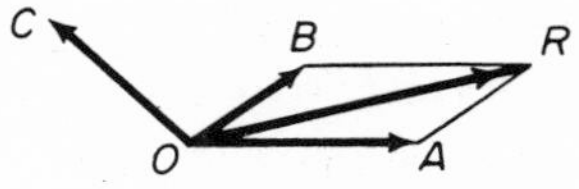

and then we form the resultant, $\overrightarrow{OS}$, of $\overrightarrow{OR}$ and $\overrightarrow{OC}$ like this:

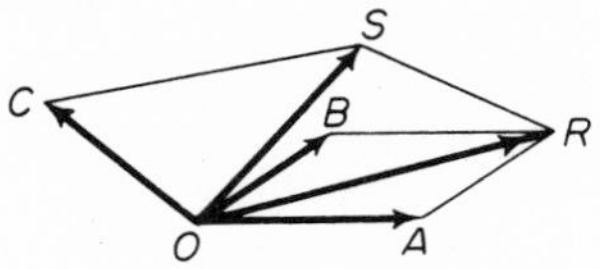

This figure looks complicated. We can simplify it by drawing only half of each parallelogram, and then even omitting the line OR, like this:

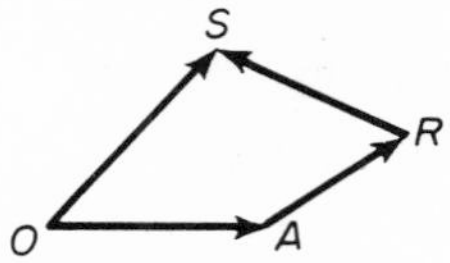

From this we see that the resultant $\overrightarrow{OS}$ can be found quickly by thinking of the vectors as free vectors and combining them by placing them end-to-end: $\overrightarrow{AR}$, which has the same magnitude and direction as $\overrightarrow{OB}$, starts where $\overrightarrow{OA}$ ends; and then $\overrightarrow{RS}$, which has the same magnitude and direction as $\overrightarrow{OC}$, starts where $\overrightarrow{AR}$ ends.

Exercise 2.7 Find, by both methods, the resultant of the vectors in Exercise 2.6, but by combining $\overrightarrow{OB}$ and $\overrightarrow{OC}$ first, and then combining their resultant with $\overrightarrow{OA}$. Prove geometrically that the resultant is the same as before.

Exercise 2.8

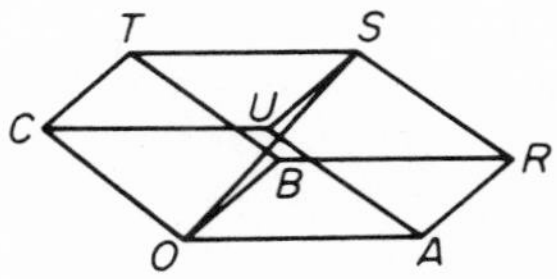

The above diagram looks like a drawing of a box. Show that if we drew only the lines OA, AR, RS, and OS we would have essentially the last figure in Exercise 2.6; that if we drew only the lines OB, BT, TS, and OS we would have a corresponding figure for Exercise 2.7; and that if we drew only OA, AU, US, and OS we would have a figure corresponding to our having first combined $\overrightarrow{OA}$ with $\overrightarrow{OC}$ and then their resultant with $\overrightarrow{OB}$.

Exercise 2.9 In Exercises 2.6, 2.7, and 2.8, is it essential that the three vectors $\overrightarrow{OA}$, $\overrightarrow{OB}$, and $\overrightarrow{OC}$ lie in a plane? Give a rule for finding the resultant of three noncoplanar vectors $\overrightarrow{OA}$, $\overrightarrow{OB}$, and $\overrightarrow{OC}$ that is analogous to the parallelogram law, and that might well be called the parallelepiped law. Prove that their resultant is the same regardless of the order in which one combines them.

Exercise 2.10 Find the resultant of the three vectors $\overrightarrow{OA}$, $\overrightarrow{OB}$, and $\overrightarrow{OC}$ below by combining them in three different orders, given that vectors $\overrightarrow{OA}$ and $\overrightarrow{OC}$ have equal magnitudes and opposite directions. Draw both the end-to-end diagrams and the full parallelogram diagrams for each case.

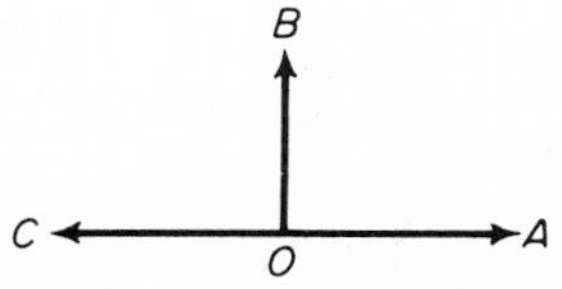

3. JOURNEYS ARE NOT VECTORS

It is all very well to start with a definition. But it is not very enlightening. Why should scientists and mathematicians be interested in objects that have magnitude and direction and combine according to the parallelogram law? Why did they even think of such objects? Indeed, do such objects exist at all —outside of the imaginations of mathematicians?

There are, of course, many objects that have both magnitude and direction. And there are, unfortunately, many books about vectors that give the reader the impression that such objects obviously and inevitably obey the parallelogram law. It is therefore worthwhile to explain carefully why most such objects do not obey this law, and then, by a process of abstraction, to find objects that do.

Suppose that I live at A and my friend lives 10 miles away at B. I start from A and walk steadily at 4 m.p.h. for $2\frac{1}{2}$ hours. Obviously, I walk 10 miles. But do I reach B?

You may say that this depends on the direction I take. But what reason is there to suppose that I keep to a fixed direction? The chances are overwhelming that I do not—unless I am preceded by a bulldozer or a heavy tank.

Most likely I walk in all sorts of directions; and almost certainly, I do not arrive at B. I may even end up at home.

Exercise 3.1 Where are all the possible places at which I can end, under the circumstances?

Now suppose that I start again from A and this time end up at B. I may take four or five hours, or I may go by bus or train and get there quickly. Never mind how I travel or how long I take. Never mind how many times I change my direction, or how tired I get, or how dirty my shoes get, or whether it rained. Ignore all such items, important though they be, and consider the abstraction that results when one concentrates solely on the fact that I start at A and end at B. Let us give this abstraction a name. What shall we call it? Not a "journey." That word reminds us too much of everyday life—of rain, and umbrellas, and vexations, and lovers meeting, and all other such items that we are ignoring here; besides, we want to preserve the word "journey" for just such an everyday concept. For our abstraction we need a neutral, colorless word. Let us call it a *shift*.

Here are routes of four journeys from A to B:

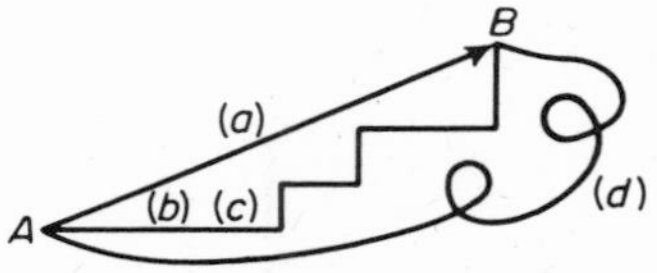

Figure 3.1

All four journeys are different—with the possible but highly improbable exception of (b) and (c).

Exercise 3.2 Why "highly improbable"?

But though the four journeys are not all the same, they yield the same shift. We can represent this shift by the arrow-headed line segment AB. It has both magnitude and direction. Indeed, it seems to have little else. Is it a vector? Let us see.

Consider three places A, B, and C as in Figure 3.2. If I walk in a straight

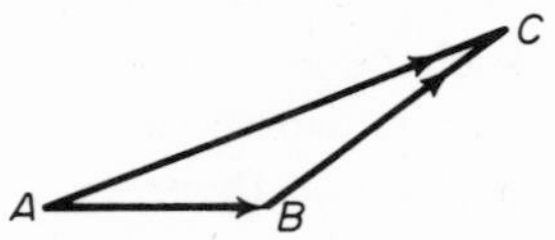

Figure 3.2

line from A to B and then in a straight line from B to C, I make a journey from A to C, but it is not the same as if I walked directly in a straight line from A to C: the scenery is different, and so is the amount of shoe leather consumed, most likely, and we can easily think of several other differences.

Exercise 3.3 Why "most likely"?

Thus, though we could say that the walks from A to B and from B to C combine to give a "resultant" journey from A to C, it is not a journey in a straight line from A to C: the walks do not combine in a way reminiscent of the way in which vectors combine; they combine more in the tautological sense that $2 + 1 = 2 + 1$ than $2 + 1 = 3$.

Journeys, then, are not vectors. But when we deal with shifts we ignore such things as the scenery and the amount of shoe leather consumed. A shift from A to B followed by a shift from B to C is indeed equivalent to a shift from A to C. And this reminds us so strongly of the vectorial situation in Figure 2.2 that we are tempted to conclude that shifts are vectors. But there is a crucial difference between the two situations. We cannot combine the above shifts in the reverse order (compare Exercise 2.5). There is no single equivalent to the shift from B to C followed by the shift from A to B. We can combine two shifts only when the second begins where the first ends. Indeed, in Figure 2.1, just as with journeys, we cannot combine a shift from O to P with one from O to Q in either order. Thus shifts are not vectors.

4. DISPLACEMENTS ARE VECTORS

Now that we have discovered why shifts are not vectors, we can easily see what further abstraction to make to obtain entities that are. From the already abstract idea of a shift, we remove the actual starting point and end point and retain only the relation between them: that B lies such and such a distance from A and in such and such a direction.* Shifts were things we invented in order to bring out certain distinctions. But this new abstraction is an accepted mathematical concept with a technical name: it is called a *displacement*. And it is a vector, as we shall now show.

In Figure 4.1, the arrow-headed line segments AB and LM are parallel and

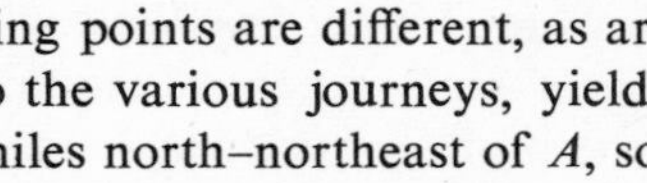

Figure 4.1

of equal length. Any journey from A to B is bound to be different from a journey from L to M. Also, the shift from A to B is different from that from L to M because the starting points are different, as are the end points. But the two shifts, and thus also the various journeys, yield the same displacement: if, for example, B is 5 miles north–northeast of A, so too is M 5 miles north–northeast of L, and the displacement is one of 5 miles in the direction north–northeast.

*We retain, too, the recollection that we are still linked, however tenuously, with journeying, for we want to retain the idea that a movement has occurred, even though we do not care at all *how* or under what circumstances it occurred.

Exercise 4.1 Starting from a point A, a man bicycles 10 miles due east to point B, stops for lunch, sells his bicycle, and then walks 10 miles due north to point C. Another man starts from B, walks 4 miles due north and 12 miles due east and then, feeling tired, and having brought along a surplus of travellers' checks, buys a car and drives 6 miles due north and 2 miles due west, ending at point D in the pouring rain. What displacement does each man undergo? [*Ans.* $10\sqrt{2}$ miles to the northeast.]

Now look at Figure 2.1. The shift from O to P followed by the shift from P to R is equivalent to the shift from O to R. The shift from P to R gives a displacement $\overrightarrow{PR}$ that is the same as the displacement $\overrightarrow{OQ}$. Therefore the displacement $\overrightarrow{OP}$ followed by the displacement $\overrightarrow{OQ}$ is equivalent to the displacement $\overrightarrow{OR}$.

Exercise 4.2 Prove, similarly, that the displacement $\overrightarrow{OQ}$ followed by the displacement $\overrightarrow{OP}$ is also equivalent to the displacement $\overrightarrow{OR}$.

Thus, displacements have magnitude and direction and combine according to the parallelogram law. According to our definition, they are therefore vectors. Since displacements such as $\overrightarrow{AB}$ and $\overrightarrow{LM}$ in Figure 4.1 are counted as identical, displacements are free vectors, and thus are somewhat special. In general, vectors such as $\overrightarrow{AB}$ and $\overrightarrow{LM}$ are not counted as identical.

5. WHY VECTORS ARE IMPORTANT

From the idea of a journey we have at last come, by a process of successive abstraction, to a specimen of a vector. The question now is whether we have come to anything worthwhile. At first sight it would seem that we have come to so pale a ghost of a journey that it could have little mathematical significance. But we must not underestimate the potency of the mathematical process of abstraction. Vectors happen to be extremely important in science and mathematics. A surprising variety of things happen to have both magnitude and direction and to combine according to the parallelogram law; and many of them are not at all reminiscent of journeys.

This should not surprise us. The process of abstraction is a powerful one. It is, indeed, a basic tool of the mathematician. Take whole numbers, for instance. Like vectors, they are abstractions. We could say that whole numbers are what is left of the idea of *apples* when we ignore not only the apple trees, the wind and the rain, the profits of cider makers, and other such items that would appear in an encyclopedia article, *but also ignore even the apples themselves*, and concentrate solely on how many there are. After we have extracted from the idea of apples the idea of whole numbers, we find that whole numbers apply to all sorts of situations that have nothing to do with apples. Much the same is true of vectors. They are more complicated than whole numbers—so are fractions, for example—but they happen to embody an important type of mathematical behavior that is widely encountered in the world around us.

To give a single example here: forces behave like vectors. This is not something obvious. A force has both magnitude and direction, of course. But this does not mean that forces necessarily combine according to the parallelogram law. That they do combine in this way is inferred from experiment.

It is worthwhile to explain what is meant when we say that forces combine according to the parallelogram law. Forces are not something visible, though their effects may be visible. They are certainly not arrow-headed line segments, though after one has worked with them mathematically for a while, one almost comes to think they are. A force can be represented by an arrow-headed line segment $\overrightarrow{OP}$ that starts at the point of application O of the force, points in the direction of the force, and has a length proportional to the magnitude of the force—for example, a length of x inches might represent a magnitude of x pounds. When a force is represented in this way, we usually avoid wordiness by talking of "the force $\overrightarrow{OP}$." But let us be more meticulous in our wording just here. To verify experimentally that forces combine according to the parallelogram law, we can make the following experiment. We arrange stationary weights and strings, and pulleys A and B, as shown, the weight W being the

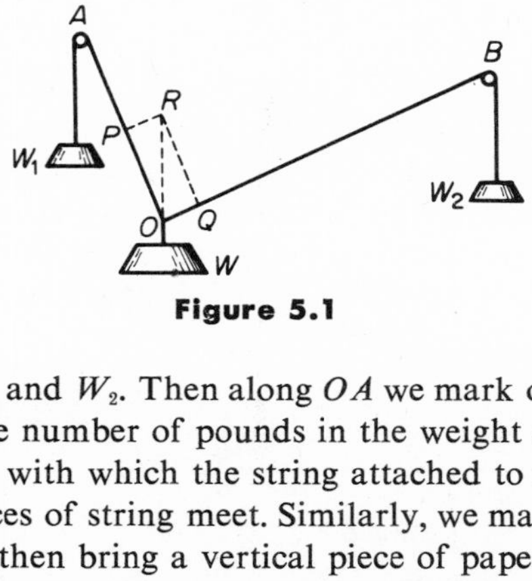

Figure 5.1

sum of the weights W_1 and W_2. Then along OA we mark off a length OP of W_1 inches, where W_1 is the number of pounds in the weight on the left and, thus, a measure of the force with which the string attached to it pulls on the point O where the three pieces of string meet. Similarly, we mark off on OB a length OQ of W_2 inches. We then bring a vertical piece of paper up to the point O, and on it complete the parallelogram defined by OP and OQ. We find that the diagonal OR is vertical and that its length in inches is W, the number of pounds in the weight in the middle. We conclude that the resultant of the forces W_1 and W_2 in the strings would just balance the weight W. Since the forces W_1 and W_2 also just balance the weight W, we say that the resultant is equivalent to the two forces. We then do the experiment over again, with different weights, and reach a similar conclusion. After that, we do it yet again; and we keep at it till our lack of patience overcomes our skepticism, upon which we say that we have proved experimentally that forces combine according to the parallelogram law. And we bolster our assertion by pointing to other experiments, of the same and different types, that indicate the same thing.

We all know that it is much easier to get through a revolving door by pushing near the outer edge than by pushing near the central axis. The effect of a force depends on its location. Home runs are scarce when the bat fails to make contact with the ball. Thus forces do not behave like free vectors. Unlike displacements, vectors representing forces such as $\overrightarrow{AB}$ and $\overrightarrow{LM}$ in Figure 4.1, though they have the same magnitude and the same direction, are not counted as equivalent. Such vectors are called *bound* vectors.

Perhaps it worries us a little that there are different kinds of vectors. Yet we have all, in our time, survived similar complications. Take numbers, for example. There are whole numbers and there are fractions. Perhaps you feel that there is not much difference between the two. Yet if we listed the properties of whole numbers and the properties of fractions we would find considerable differences. For instance, if we divide fractions by fractions the results are always fractions, but this statement does not remain true if we replace the word "fractions" by "whole numbers." Worse, every whole number has a next higher one, but no fraction has a next higher fraction, for between any two fractions we can always slip infinitely many others. Even so, when trying to define *number* we might be inclined to insist that, given any two different numbers, one of them will always be the smaller and the other the larger. Yet when we become more sophisticated and expand our horizons to include complex numbers like $2 + 3\sqrt{-1}$, we have to give up even this property of being greater or smaller, which at first seemed an absolutely essential part of the idea of number. With vectors too, not only are there various types, but we shall learn that not every one of their attributes that seems at this stage to be essential is in fact so. One of the things that gives mathematics its power is the shedding of attributes that turn out not to be essential, for this, after all, is just the process of abstraction.

Exercise 5.1 Find the resultants of the following displacements:

(a) 3 ft. due east and 3 ft. due north. [*Ans.* $3\sqrt{2}$ ft. to the northeast.]

(b) 5 ft. due north and 5 ft. due east.

(c) 9 cm. to the right and $9\sqrt{3}$ cm. vertically upwards. [*Ans.* 18 cm. in an upward direction making 60° with the horizontal towards the right.]

(d) 9 cm. to the left and $9\sqrt{3}$ cm. vertically downward.

(e) the resultants in parts (c) and (d).

(f) x units positively along the x-axis and y units positively along the y-axis. [*Ans.* $\sqrt{x^2 + y^2}$ units in the direction making an angle $\tan^{-1} y/x$ with the positive x-axis.]

Exercise 5.2 Like Exercise 5.1 for the following:

(a) 8 km. to the left and 3 km. to the left.

(b) 5 fathoms vertically downward and 2 fathoms vertically upward.

(c) α units to the right and β units to the left. [There are three different cases. What are they? Show how they can be summed up in one statement.]

(d) h miles 60° north of east and h miles 60° south of east.

Exercise 5.3 What single force is equivalent to the following three horizontal forces acting on a particle at a point O? (1) magnitude 1 lb. pulling to the north; (2) magnitude 1 lb. pulling to the east; (3) magnitude $\sqrt{2}$ lb. pulling to the northwest. [*Ans.* 2 lbs. acting at point O and pulling to the north.]

Exercise 5.4 What force combined with a force at a point 0 of 1 lb. pulling to the east will yield a resultant force of 2 lbs. pulling in a direction 60° north of east?

Exercise 5.5 Vector $\overrightarrow{OP}$ has magnitude $2a$ and points to the right in a direction 30° above the horizontal. What vector combined with it will yield a vertical resultant, $\overrightarrow{OR}$, of magnitude $2\sqrt{3}\,a$?

Exercise 5.6 Find two forces at a point O, one vertical and one horizontal, that have a resultant of magnitude h, making 45° with the horizontal force. [*Ans.* The forces have magnitude $h/\sqrt{2}$.]

Exercise 5.7 Find two forces at a point O, one vertical and one horizontal, that have a resultant of magnitude h that makes an angle of 30° with the horizontal force.

Exercise 5.8 Find two displacements, one parallel to the x-axis and the other to the y-axis, that yield a resultant displacement of magnitude h ft. making a positive acute angle α with the positive x-direction.

Exercise 5.9 What is the resultant of n vectors, each starting at the point O, each having magnitude h, and each pointing to the pole star? [We could have shortened this by asking for the resultant of n equal vectors. But we have not yet defined "equal" vectors—even though we have already spoken of the equality of free vectors! You may find it instructive to try to do so here; but be warned that it is not as easy as it seems, and that there is something lacking in the wording of the question.]

Exercise 5.10 A particle is acted on by two forces, one of them to the west and of magnitude 1 dyne, and the other in the direction 60° north of east and of magnitude 2 dynes. What third force acting on the particle would keep it in equilibrium (i. e., what third force would make the resultant of all three forces have zero magnitude)? [*Ans.* Magnitude $\sqrt{3}$ dynes pointing due south.]

6. THE SINGULAR INCIDENT OF THE VECTORIAL TRIBE

It is rumored that there was once a tribe of Indians who believed that arrows are vectors. To shoot a deer due northeast, they did not aim an arrow in the northeasterly direction; they sent two arrows simultaneously, one due north and the other due east, relying on the powerful resultant of the two arrows to kill the deer.

Skeptical scientists have doubted the truth of this rumor, pointing out that not the slightest trace of the tribe has ever been found. But the complete disappearance of the tribe through starvation is precisely what one would expect under the circumstances; and since the theory that the tribe existed confirms two such diverse things as the NONVECTORIAL BEHAVIOR OF ARROWS and the DARWINIAN PRINCIPLE OF NATURAL SELECTION, it is surely not a theory to be dismissed lightly.

Exercise 6.1 Arrow-headed line segments have magnitude and direction and are used to represent vectors. Why are they nevertheless not vectors?

Exercise 6.2 Given the three vectors represented by $\overrightarrow{OP}$, $\overrightarrow{OQ}$, and $\overrightarrow{OR}$ in Figure 2.1, form three new entities having the same respective directions, but having magnitudes equal to five times the magnitudes of the respective vectors. Prove geometrically that these new entities are so related that the third is a diagonal of the parallelogram having the other two as adjacent sides.

Exercise 6.3 If in Exercise 6.2 the new entities had the same respective directions as the vectors represented by $\overrightarrow{OP}$, $\overrightarrow{OQ}$, and $\overrightarrow{OR}$, but had magnitudes that were one unit greater than the magnitudes of the corresponding vectors, show that the new entities would not be such that the third was a diagonal of the parallelogram having the other two as adjacent sides.

Exercise 6.4 Suppose we represented vectors by arrow-headed line segments that had the same starting points and directions as the vectors, but had lengths proportional to the squares of the magnitudes of the vectors, so that, for example, if a force of 1 lb. were represented by a segment of length 1 inch, then a force of 2 lbs. would be represented by one of 4 inches. Show that, in general, these representations of vectors would not obey the parallelogram law. Note that the statement of the parallelogram law in Section 2 therefore needs amending, and amend it accordingly. [If you think carefully, you will realize that this is a topsy-turvy question since, in proving the required result, you will assume that the vectors, when "properly" represented, obey the parallelogram law; and thus, in a sense, you will assume the very amendment you are seeking. But since you have probably been assuming the amendment all this while, you will be able to think your way through. The purpose of this exercise is to draw your attention to this rarely mentioned, usually assumed amendment.]

7. SOME AWKWARD QUESTIONS

When are two vectors equal? The answer depends on what we choose to mean by the word "equal"—we are the masters, not the word. But we do not want to use the word in an outrageous sense: for example, we would not want to say that two vectors are equal if they are mentioned in the same sentence.

Choosing a meaning for the word "equal" here is not as easy as one might imagine. For example, we could reasonably say that two vectors having the same magnitudes, identical directions, and a common starting point are equal vectors. And if one of the vectors were somehow pink and the other green, we would probably be inclined to ignore the colors and say that the vectors were still equal. But what if one of the vectors represented a force and the other a displacement? There would then be two difficulties.

The first difficulty is that the vector representing a displacement would be a free vector, but the one representing the force would not. If, in Figure 4.1, we counted free vectors represented by $\overrightarrow{AB}$ and $\overrightarrow{LM}$ as equal, we might find ourselves implying that forces represented by $\overrightarrow{AB}$ and $\overrightarrow{LM}$ were also equal, though actually they have different effects. [Even so, it is extremely convenient to say such things as "a force acts at A and an equal force acts at L." We shall not do so in this book. But one can get by with saying such things once one has explained what is awkward about them, just as, in trigonometry one gets by with writing $\sin^2 \theta$ after one has explained that this does not stand for $\sin(\sin \theta)$ but $(\sin \theta)^2$.]

As for the second difficulty about the idea of the equality of vectors, it takes us back to the definition of a vector. For if, in Figure 2.1, $\overrightarrow{OP}$ represents a force and $\overrightarrow{OQ}$ a displacement, the two vectors will not combine by the parallelogram law at all. We know this from experiments with forces. But we can appreciate the awkwardness of the situation by merely asking ourselves what the resultant would be if they did combine in this way. A "disforcement"?* [Compare Exercise 5.9.]

If two vectors are to be called equal, it seems reasonable to require that they be able to combine with each other. The situation is not the same as it is with numbers. Although 3 apples and 3 colors are different things, we can say that the numbers 3 are equal in the sense that, if we assign a pebble to each of the apples, these pebbles will exactly suffice for doing the same with the colors. And in this sense we can indeed combine 3 apples and 3 colors—not to yield 6 apples, or 6 colors, or 6 colored apples [it would surely be only 3 colored apples], but 6 *items*. There does not seem to be a corresponding sense in which we could reasonably combine a vector representing a force with one representing a displacement, quite apart from the question of bound versus free vectors: there does not seem to be a vectorial analogue of the numerical

*Actually, of course, lack of a name proves no more than that if the resultant exists, it has not hitherto been deemed important enough to warrant a name.

concept of a countable item.*

Though $\overrightarrow{OP}$ and $\overrightarrow{OQ}$ do not combine according to the parallelogram law if, for example, $\overrightarrow{OP}$ represents a force and $\overrightarrow{OQ}$ a displacement, they nevertheless represent vectors. Evidently our definition of a vector needs even further amendment. We might seek to avoid trouble by retreating to the definition of a vector as "an entity having both magnitude and direction," without mentioning the parallelogram law. But once we start retreating, where do we stop? Why not be content to define a vector as "an entity having direction," or as "an entity having magnitude," or, with Olympian simplicity, as just "an entity"? Alternatively, we could make the important distinction between the abstract mathematical concept of a vector and entities, such as forces, that behave like these abstract vectors and are called *vector quantities*. This helps, but it does not solve the present problem so much as sweep it under the rug. We might amend our definition of a vector by saying that vectors combine according to the parallelogram law only with vectors of the same kind: forces with forces, displacements with displacements, accelerations (which are vectors) with accelerations, and so on. But even that is tricky since, for example, in dynamics we learn that force equals mass times acceleration. So we would have to allow for the fact that though a force does not combine with an acceleration, it does combine with a vector of the type mass-times-acceleration in dynamics.

We shall return to this matter. (See Section 8 of Chapter 2.) But enough of such questions here. If we continue to fuss with the definition we shall never get started. Even if we succeeded in patching up the definition to meet this particular emegency, other emergencies would arise later. The best thing to do is to keep an open mind and learn to live with a flexible situation, and even to relish it as something akin to the true habitat of the best research.

*Even with numbers there are complications. For example, 3 ft. and 3 inches can be said to yield 6 items; yet in another sense they yield 39 inches, $3\frac{1}{4}$ ft., and so on—and each of these can also be regarded as a number of items, though the $3\frac{1}{4}$ involves a further subtlety. Consider also 3 ft. and 3 lbs., and then 2.38477 ft. and 2.38477 lbs.

2

ALGEBRAIC NOTATION AND BASIC IDEAS

1. EQUALITY AND ADDITION

Instead of denoting vectors by symbols like $\overrightarrow{OA}$ and $\overrightarrow{PQ}$, it is often convenient to denote them by single letters printed in bold-face type, like this: **U**, **V**. (In written work, some people place semi-arrows above ordinary capital letters, as $\vec{U}$, $\vec{V}$. Others write double lines on the letters, like this: $\mathbb{U}$, $\mathbb{V}$. Yet others place lines underneath the letters: $\underline{U}$, $\underline{V}$.)

Let us agree to say that two vectors, **U** and **V**, are *equal* if they have equal magnitudes, identical directions, and a common starting point, and represent types of entities that can combine with each other according to the parallelogram law. If they are free vectors we need not insist that they have a common starting point.

We denote this equality by the familiar symbol $=$, writing, for example,

$$\overrightarrow{OA} = \overrightarrow{OB}, \qquad \mathbf{U} = \mathbf{V}. \tag{1.1}$$

We shall also use this symbol $=$ in the broader sense of "equivalent to" as the phrase was used in the statement of the parallelogram law in Chapter 1. Also, of course, we shall use the symbol in its usual arithmetical and algebraic sense, as in $2 + 2 = 4$.

Exercise 1.1 In the definition of equal vectors, what do you think we mean by "equal magnitudes"? Consider, for example, magnitudes of 6 ft., 6 lbs., and 2 yds.

The magnitude of a vector $\overrightarrow{OA}$ is usually denoted by $|OA|$ or just plain OA, and that of a vector **V** by V.

Exercise 1.2 If **U** and **V** have the same starting point and *the same direction*, show that the magnitude of their resultant is $U + V$.

Note that we did not say in Exercise 1.2 that **U** and **V** were capable of having a resultant: **U** might have been a force and **V** a displacement, for example. Let us agree to assume that vectors in a given problem or discussion can combine unless the contrary is either obvious or else explicitly stated.

When vectors are related as in Exercise 1.2, their resultant is akin to a sum. For this reason, and for others that will appear later, it is appropriate to denote the combination of vectors according to the parallelogram law by the familiar symbol $+$. Thus, if $\overrightarrow{OR}$ is the resultant of $\overrightarrow{OP}$ and $\overrightarrow{OQ}$, as in Figure 2.1 of Chapter 1, we write:

$$\overrightarrow{OP} + \overrightarrow{OQ} = \overrightarrow{OR}, \tag{1.2}$$

and we even use arithmetical language, saying that we *add* the vectors $\overrightarrow{OP}$ and $\overrightarrow{OQ}$ and that their *sum* is $\overrightarrow{OR}$.

From Exercise 2.5 of Chapter 1, we see that

$$\mathbf{U} + \mathbf{V} = \mathbf{V} + \mathbf{U}. \tag{1.3}$$

Technically, we refer to this fact by saying that vectorial addition is *commutative*.

Exercise 1.3 Show geometrically that vectorial addition is *associative*, that is,

$$(\mathbf{U} + \mathbf{V}) + \mathbf{W} = \mathbf{U} + (\mathbf{V} + \mathbf{W}). \tag{1.4}$$

Also write out what this relation says using the language of Chapter 1, e. g., resultant, combination, etc. [Note that we have not defined the symbol "("and the symbol")": their significance is easily guessed here.]

2. MULTIPLICATION BY NUMBERS

The resultant of **V** and **V** is a vector identical with **V** except that its magnitude is twice as great. We denote it by 2**V**, and this allows us to write the satisfactory equation:

$$\mathbf{V} + \mathbf{V} = 2\mathbf{V}.$$

Similarly, we denote the resultant of **V**, **V**, and **V** by 3**V**, and so on.

Exercise 2.1 Show that $2\mathbf{V} + \mathbf{V} = 3\mathbf{V}$.

Exercise 2.2 Describe $5\mathbf{V}$ in terms of $\mathbf{V}$.

If

$$3\mathbf{U} = 2\mathbf{V}$$

we write

$$\mathbf{U} = \frac{2}{3}\mathbf{V}, \quad \text{and} \quad \mathbf{V} = \frac{3}{2}\mathbf{U};$$

more generally, if a and b are positive whole numbers, and

$$a\mathbf{U} = b\mathbf{V}, \tag{2.1}$$

we write

$$\mathbf{U} = \frac{b}{a}\mathbf{V} \quad \text{and} \quad \mathbf{V} = \frac{a}{b}\mathbf{U}. \tag{2.2}$$

Exercise 2.3 Show that $3(\frac{2}{3}\mathbf{V}) = 2\mathbf{V}$. [*Hint.* Start by expressing the left-hand side in terms of $\mathbf{U}$ as in the preceding paragraph.]

Exercise 2.4 Show that if a and b are positive whole numbers,

$$a\left(\frac{b}{a}\mathbf{V}\right) = b\mathbf{V}.$$

Exercise 2.5 Describe $\frac{2}{3}\mathbf{V}$ in terms of $\mathbf{V}$.

Exercise 2.6 Show that if a and b are positive whole numbers, then $(b/a)\mathbf{V}$ is a vector identical with $\mathbf{V}$ except that its magnitude is $(b/a)V$.

If h is a positive number, we write $h\mathbf{V}$ for the vector that is identical with $\mathbf{V}$ except that its magnitude is h times that of $\mathbf{V}$. It may seem that this is merely a repetition of the result of Exercise 2.6, and contains no more than is contained in Equations (2.1) and (2.2); for we have only to express h as a fraction b/a, where a and b are whole numbers, in order to link up with those equations. But not every number can be expressed as such a fraction. Those that can are called *rational* numbers, and the amount of rational numbers is negligible compared with the amount of numbers that cannot be so expressed. The latter are called *irrational* numbers, examples being $\sqrt{2}$ and π. A book about vectors is not the place for a discussion of irrational numbers. One can do arithmetic with them much as one does with rational numbers, and the general case $h\mathbf{V}$ can be regarded as a valid extension of the ideas embodied in Equations (2.1) and (2.2). If we feel so inclined, we can amend the definition of a vector to include the idea of $h\mathbf{V}$ where h is irrational. We say that $h\mathbf{V}$ is the result of *multiplying* the vector $\mathbf{V}$ by the number h.

Exercise 2.7 Let the vector $\mathbf{V}$ point along the x-axis. Form two new vectors, the first by rotating $\mathbf{V}$ about its starting point through 45° towards the positive y-direction, and the second by rotating $\mathbf{V}$ similarly through 45° towards the negative y-direction. Show that the resultant of these two vectors is $\sqrt{2}\,\mathbf{V}$.

Exercise 2.8 What would be the resultant if we did Exercise 2.7 starting not with **V** but with $\sqrt{2}\,\mathbf{V}$?

Exercise 2.9 Show by means of a diagram that multiplication of vectors by numbers obeys the *distributive* law:

$$h(\mathbf{U} + \mathbf{V}) = h\mathbf{U} + h\mathbf{V}. \tag{2.3}$$

[This can not be proved just by noting its similarity to a familiar algebraic equation. For a hint, compare Exercise 6.2 of Chapter 1, which is a special case of this theorem.]

Exercise 2.10 If **U** and **V** both start at the origin and have equal magnitudes, **U** pointing along the positive x-axis and **V** along the positive y-axis, and if a and b are positive numbers, what is the tangent of the angle that the vector $a\mathbf{U} + b\mathbf{V}$ makes with the x-axis?

3. SUBTRACTION

Having managed to relate the symbol + to the parallelogram law without doing violence to its usual arithmetical meaning, we wonder whether we can be as successful with the symbol −. It turns out that we can. If **V** is a vector, we define its negative, which we write $-\mathbf{V}$, as a vector identical with it except that it points in the opposite direction. Thus in Figure 3.1, if **U** is **V** turned

Figure 3.1

through 180°, then $\mathbf{U} = -\mathbf{V}$. Note that **V** and $-\mathbf{V}$ have the same magnitude: the magnitude is always taken to be positive (when it is not zero, of course). To consolidate the link between the arithmetical and vectorial uses of the symbol −, we define $(-h)\mathbf{V}$ for positive h as $h(-\mathbf{V})$.

Exercise 3.1 If $\mathbf{U} = -\mathbf{V}$, show that $\mathbf{V} = -\mathbf{U}$. What is $-(-\mathbf{V})$?

Exercise 3.2 What is the resultant of $2\mathbf{V}$ and $-\mathbf{V}$? [*Ans.* **V**.]

Exercise 3.3 Prove that if h is positive, $h(-\mathbf{V}) = -(h\mathbf{V})$.

Exercise 3.4 What is the resultant of $a\mathbf{V}$ and $-b\mathbf{V}$?

We denote a vector of zero magnitude by the symbol 0, without bothering to use bold-face type. A zero vector, as it is called, does not quite fit our definition of a vector since it has no direction or, thought of in another way, it has all directions. We count it as a vector nevertheless, and we shall not pause to patch up the definition of a vector to accomodate it.

Exercise 3.5 What is the resultant of **V** and $-\mathbf{V}$? What is the resultant in Exercise 3.4 if $a = b$?

Exercise 3.6 Show that $\mathbf{V} + O = O + \mathbf{V} = \mathbf{V}$.

We now define $\mathbf{U} - \mathbf{V}$ as $\mathbf{U} + (-\mathbf{V})$, and say that to *subtract* $\mathbf{V}$ we add $-\mathbf{V}$. Since this subtraction is thus essentially a type of vectorial addition, it obeys the same rules as vectorial addition. For example,

$$(\mathbf{U} + \mathbf{V}) - \mathbf{W} = \mathbf{U} + (\mathbf{V} - \mathbf{W})$$

and

$$h(\mathbf{U} - \mathbf{V}) = h\mathbf{U} - h\mathbf{V}.$$

Exercise 3.7 Consider the discussion of the equality of vectors in Section 7 of Chapter 1 in the light of the reasonable requirement that if $\mathbf{U} = \mathbf{V}$ then $\mathbf{U} - \mathbf{V} = 0$.

Exercise 3.8 If $\mathbf{U} + \mathbf{V} = \mathbf{W}$, show that $\mathbf{U} = \mathbf{W} - \mathbf{V}$, first by means of a diagram involving two overlapping parallelograms, and second by the purely algebraic manipulation of adding $-\mathbf{V}$ to both sides of the equation and using the results of Exercises 3.5 and 3.6.

For displacements it is easy to see that

$$\overrightarrow{AB} = -\overrightarrow{BA}, \tag{3.1}$$

though if $\overrightarrow{AB}$ were not a free vector this would, in general, not be true, since $\overrightarrow{BA}$ starts at B while $\overrightarrow{AB}$ starts at A.

Again, the resultant of the three displacements $\overrightarrow{AB}$, $\overrightarrow{BC}$ and $\overrightarrow{CD}$ is the dis-

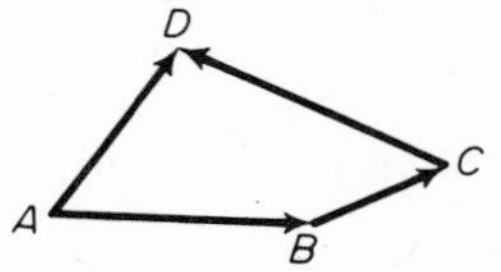

placement $\overrightarrow{AD}$. (Note that this is true even if A, B, C, and D do not lie in a plane.) Let D coincide with A. Then the resultant is zero. Therefore for any displacements $\overrightarrow{AB}$, $\overrightarrow{BC}$, $\overrightarrow{CA}$,

$$\overrightarrow{AB} + \overrightarrow{BC} + \overrightarrow{CA} = 0. \tag{3.2}$$

Suppose we replace the displacement $\overrightarrow{BC}$ by the algebraic expression $c - b$, $\overrightarrow{CA}$ by $a - c$, and $\overrightarrow{AB}$ by $b - a$. Then from Equations (3.1) and (3.2) we obtain the formally valid equations

$$b - a = -(a - b) \tag{3.3}$$

and

$$(c - b) + (a - c) + (b - a) = 0. \tag{3.4}$$

Exercise 3.9 For displacements, show that $\overrightarrow{AB} + \overrightarrow{BC} + \overrightarrow{CD} + \overrightarrow{DE} = \overrightarrow{AE}$, write down the analogous algebraic equation, and verify that it is satisfied.

Later we shall see that this sort of relationship between displacement equations and algebraic equations is not accidental. We can begin to see why by considering vectors in a one-dimensional space.

Exercise 3.10 If A and B are points on the x-axis with x-coordinates a and b respectively, and $b > a$, show that the magnitude of the displacement $\overrightarrow{AB}$ is $b - a$.

In one dimension, there are only two possible directions. Vectors confined to the x-axis, for example, can point to the right or to the left, but in no other direction. We could give these directions labels such as "right" and "left," or "first" and "second." But it is much more pleasing to label them "+" and "—." For example, in Exercise 3.10, the quantity $b - a$, being positive, can now be taken to describe not just the magnitude of the displacement $\overrightarrow{AB}$ but also its direction; while if we similarly relate the displacement $\overrightarrow{BA}$ to $a - b$, this quantity, being negative, gives both the magnitude and direction of $\overrightarrow{BA}$.

Exercise 3.11 Show that $b - a$ in Exercise 3.10 represents both the magnitude and direction of the displacement $\overrightarrow{AB}$ whether $b > a$ or not.

Exercise 3.12 In Exercise 3.11, if O is the origin, show that $\overrightarrow{AB} = \overrightarrow{OB} - \overrightarrow{OA}$, *no matter what the relative positions of O, A, and B on the x-axis.* [Do this first by deducing it from Equation (3.2) with O replacing C, and second, by considering the corresponding algebraic relation.]

No longer confining ourselves to one dimension, we have, from Equations (3.1) and (3.2),

$$\overrightarrow{AB} + \overrightarrow{CA} = -\overrightarrow{BC}$$

so that, by Equation (3.1),

$$\overrightarrow{AB} - \overrightarrow{AC} = \overrightarrow{CB}. \tag{3.5}$$

This gives us a convenient way to draw the difference of two displacements, $\overrightarrow{AB} - \overrightarrow{AC}$. We merely draw $\overrightarrow{AB}$ and $\overrightarrow{AC}$ and join their tips from C to B (not B to C), as in Figure 3.2.

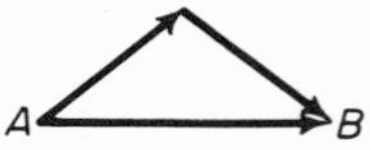

Figure 3.2

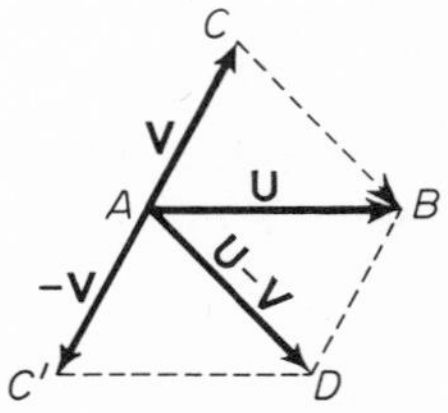

Figure 3.3

For vectors that are not free vectors but are tied to a particular starting point, the preceding still gives the magnitude and direction of their difference though not its location. Thus in Figure 3.3, if vectors **U**, **V** are represented by $\overrightarrow{AB}$, $\overrightarrow{AC}$ and we wish to find **U** − **V**, we should first construct − **V** by turning $\overrightarrow{AC}$ about A through 180° to the position AC'. Then we should complete the parallelogram $AC'DB$ to obtain **U** − **V** as the vector represented by the diagonal $\overrightarrow{AD}$. But since triangles $AC'D$ and CAB are congruent, and CAC' is a straight line, it is easy to prove that CB and AD are parallel and of equal length. So we can find the magnitude and direction of **U** − **V** precisely as in Figure 3.2, and this is all we need since we already know it starts at A. [Compare Exercise 3.8.]

Exercise 3.13 Prove that triangles $AC'D$ and CAB are congruent, and that CB and AD are parallel and of equal length.

Exercise 3.14 Find the magnitudes and directions of **U** − **V** in the following cases. [Use the method of Figure 3.2.]

(a) **U** has magnitude 5 and points northeast; **V** has magnitude 5 and points northwest. [*Ans.* magnitude $5\sqrt{2}$; pointing east.]

(b) **U** has magnitude $8\sqrt{3}$ and points east; **V** has magnitude 16 and points 30° north of east.

(c) **U** has magnitude 7 and points 20° north of east; **V** has magnitude $7\sqrt{2}$ and points 65° north of east.

Exercise 3.15 A force of 8 lbs. acts along the positive direction of the x-axis. If it acts on a particle at the origin, what force combined with it would produce on the particle a resultant force of 8 lbs. pulling along the positive y-axis? [If the resultant force is **R**, the given force **X**, and the required force **Y**, then $\mathbf{X} + \mathbf{Y} = \mathbf{R}$; so $\mathbf{Y} = \mathbf{R} - \mathbf{X}$, whose magnitude and direction can be found by the method of Figure 3.2.]

Exercise 3.16 Like Exercise 3.15 but with the resultant making 60° with the positive x-direction.

4. SPEED AND VELOCITY

In ordinary conversation we usually make no distinction between *speed* and *velocity*. In fact, most dictionaries treat the two words as synonymous. But in the physical sciences, speed and velocity have different meanings. Speed is the rate at which distance is covered per unit time, but velocity involves the direction also. Thus 5 m. p. h. is a speed, but 5 m. p. h. vertically upward is a velocity, and it is a different velocity from 5 m. p. h. in any other direction. A point moving with constant speed in a circle does not have an unchanging velocity: the velocity changes because its direction changes.

Figure 4.1 shows a platform with a line AB marked on it. Suppose a point

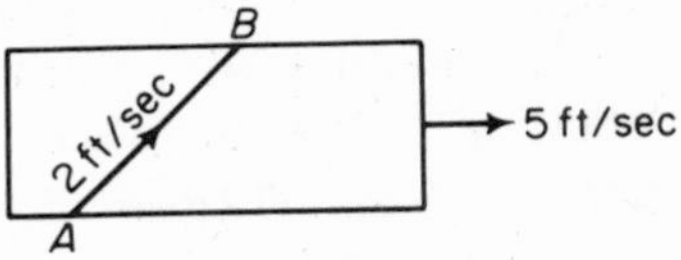

Figure 4.1

moves uniformly along this line from A to B at 2 ft./sec., and that the platform moves uniformly to the east at 5 ft./sec. relative to the ground. Then the point is being subjected to two different velocities at the same time. But it does not, therefore, move relative to the ground in two different directions at once. To say that it did would be to speak nonsense (except, perhaps, if we were talking of quantum phenomena, which we are not). It would remind us of the humorist Stephen Leacock's famous account of the angry man who "flung himself from the room, flung himself upon his horse and rode madly off in all directions."

How does the point actually move? We can find out by considering what happens in one second. For convenience, let us assume that AB is of length 2 ft., so that in one second the point goes from A to B. During this second, the platform moves 5 ft. to the east, and the ends of the line AB drawn on it move to new positions, A', B', that are 5 ft. to the east of their original positions, as in Figure 4.2. The moving point travels from A to B' relative to the ground.

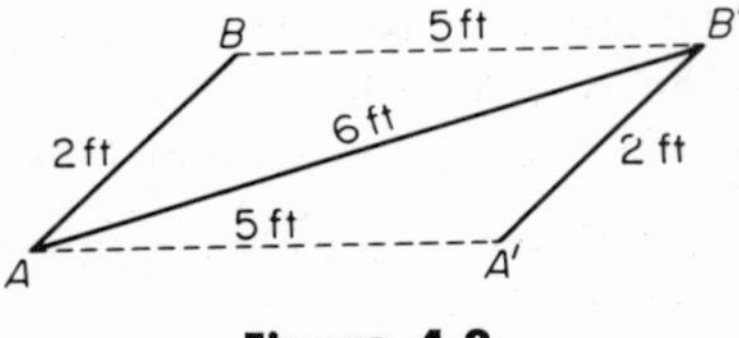

Figure 4.2

The distance AB' depends on the angle BAA'; for simplicity, let us suppose that the distance comes to 6 ft. It is easy to see that the point travels from A to B' in a straight line, with uniform speed relative to the ground.

> **Exercise 4.1** Prove this. [To get the idea, consider first what happens in, say, $\frac{1}{2}$ sec., using similar triangles. Then consider what happens in t secs.]

Figure 4.2 tells what happens in 1 sec. Let us, so to speak, divide it by 1 sec.—that is, let us replace ft. by ft./sec. wherever it occurs there. Then $\overrightarrow{AB}$ will represent the velocity of the point along AB relative to the platform, $\overrightarrow{AA'}$ the velocity of the platform relative to the ground, and $\overrightarrow{AB'}$ that of the point relative to the ground. And we see that the first two combine by the parallelogram law to yield the third. In this sense, then, we may regard velocities as vector quantities.

Exercise 4.2 Show that had Figure 4.2 been drawn to illustrate what happens in t sec., the distances would be $2t$ ft., $5t$ ft., and $6t$ ft., but the ultimate relationship between the velocities would be the same as before.

Exercise 4.3 A train is going at 50 m. p. h. due north, and a fly in one of the compartments flies at 20 m. p. h. northeast relative to the compartment. Find, by means of an accurate diagram, the actual velocity of the fly relative to the rails.

Exercise 4.4 In Exercise 4.3, if the fly had been flying at 20 m. p. h. northeast relative to the rails, find, graphically, its velocity relative to the compartment.

Exercise 4.5 A cyclist goes at 8 m. p. h. due east, and the wind is blowing at 10 m. p. h. due east. What is the velocity of the wind relative to the cyclist? What would it be if he turned around and travelled due west at 8 m. p. h.?

Exercise 4.6 Like Exercise 4.5, but with the wind blowing due south at 8 m. p. h.

Exercise 4.7 A cyclist goes at 6 m. p. h. due north and feels the wind coming against him with a relative velocity of 4 m. p. h. due west. What is the actual velocity of the wind?

Exercise 4.8 The wind is blowing due south with a speed of 9 ft./sec. How fast must a car travel due east in order that the wind shall have, relative to the car, a speed of 15 ft./sec.?

Exercise 4.9 A gun mounted on a train is pointed vertically upward. The train moves horizontally due east at 80 m. p. h. and the gun fires a bullet with a muzzle velocity of 80 m. p. h. What is the velocity of the bullet relative to the ground? [*Ans.* Since the bullet has the velocity of the gun, and thus of the train, as well as its vertical muzzle velocity relative to the gun, its velocity relative to the ground is $80\sqrt{2}$ m. p. h. toward the east at 45° to the horizontal.]

Exercise 4.10 Rain is falling vertically with a speed of u ft./sec. At what angle does it appear to be falling as viewed from a train moving horizontally at v ft./sec.? [*Ans.* At $\tan^{-1}(u/v)$ to the horizontal.]

Exercise 4.11 The wind is blowing steadily from the east at 5 m. p. h. A boat in still water is travelling in a circle, with a constant speed of 5 m. p. h. A pennant is flying at the top of the mast. Describe in words the way the direction of the pennant changes (a) relative to the deck of the boat, and (b) relative to the water. [It was a situation like this that led the astronomer Bradley to an understanding of the phenomenon of *aber-*

ration, a topic you may find well worth looking into on your own. Note that the velocities in parts (a) and (b) both change.]

Exercise 4.12 In Exercise 4.10, if the rain were falling at an angle of θ to the horizontal, show that its apparent direction would make with its actual direction an angle $\sin^{-1}\{(u/v)\sin\theta\}$. [Compare this with the astronomical phenomenon of aberration which may be briefly described as follows: To catch the light from a star, a telescope must point in the apparent direction of the incoming light. Consequently, as the earth moves in its orbit the stars seem to move once a year in tiny ovals (actually ellipses) whose shapes depend on θ, and thus on the positions of the stars.]

It is customary to define velocity as *the rate of change of displacement with respect to time*. Let us consider it from this point of view. If a point moves uniformly along a straight line from P to Q, a distance of s ft., in t sec., it has a speed of s ft./t sec. or $\frac{s}{t}$ ft./sec. Its velocity is a quantity having the direction of the displacement $\overrightarrow{PQ}$ but a magnitude of $\frac{s}{t}$ ft./sec., which is $1/t$ times the magnitude of $\overrightarrow{PQ}$ and is, in fact, the speed. The displacement $\overrightarrow{PQ}$ combines with other displacements of the point according to the parallelogram law; and changing the magnitudes of these displacements by a factor $1/t$ will clearly yield entities that also combine according to the parallelogram law. So velocities, as here defined, are vector quantities.

The velocity vector above can be denoted by $(1/t)\,\overrightarrow{PQ}$, and this is reminiscent of the multiplication of a vector by a number. There is a difference, though. Vectors $5\mathbf{V}$ and $\mathbf{V}$ can combine with one another, but $\overrightarrow{PQ}$ and $(1/t)\,\overrightarrow{PQ}$ can not: the former is a displacement, and we have been measuring its magnitude here in ft.; but the latter is a velocity and its magnitude is not a length but a speed, here measured in ft./sec.

Suppose the motion is not uniform. Then when we divide the distance gone by the time taken we get the *average* speed. Correspondingly, we can define the *average* velocity as $(1/t)\,PQ$. But this average velocity has an unexpected property. If I walk 10 miles in 2 hours my average speed is 5 m. p. h. But unless I walk in a straight line, my average velocity does not have a magnitude of 5 m. p. h. This is because my displacement is less than 10 miles if I change direction. If I walk a circuitous path and, having gone my 10 miles, end up where I started, I may end up exhausted from averaging 5 m. p. h. up hill and down dale for 2 solid hours, but my average velocity comes to zero.

I think we simply have to accept the fact that the vectorial concept of average velocity has unpleasant aspects when applied to motion not in a straight line. When motion is uniform, the speed is the same at every instant. When the motion is not uniform, the concept of *instantaneous* speed is a rather sophisticated one. It involves ideas belonging to the calculus into which we can not go here; but roughly speaking, the instantaneous speed is the value that the average speed approaches as the time interval gets smaller and smaller.

When these ideas are applied to the average velocity, they yield an *instantaneous* velocity that, except in highly artificial situations, behaves much as one would expect it to behave, and this despite the peculiar characteristics of the average velocity from which it is obtained. The instantaneous velocity is a vector quantity, and its magnitude is the instantaneous speed. At every instant, it has the direction of the line tangent to the path of the moving point at the instantaneous position of the point.

There is a subtle difference between velocity considered in terms of the moving platform and velocity defined as the rate of change of displacement with respect to time. Look back at the discussion of the former, and at the exercises based on it, and you will see that in each case the three velocities that are involved in the parallelogram law are not all measured with respect to the same standard of reference. In the platform situation, for example, the 5 ft./sec. and the 6 ft./sec. are velocities relative to the ground, but the 2 ft./sec. is a velocity relative to the moving platform. With the definition in terms of displacements, the three velocities in a parallelogram-law relationship are really velocities with respect to the same standard of reference.* This may well seem like an unimportant distinction, especially since the two approaches to the concept of velocity both lead to the theorem that velocity is a vector quantity, and both yield the same resultant for two given velocities. But actually the distinction is a basic one physically. The resultants are the same only because of the nature of Newtonian space and time. In Einstein's special theory of relativity, the resultants are different.

When defined in terms of displacements, velocities, like displacements, are free vectors. Yet in physical situations it seems essential to give velocity a specific location. For example, the velocity of a particle should surely be located at the particle and thus be represented by an arrow-headed line segment starting at the particle. In a storm, the velocity of the air is different at different places. To regard velocity as a free vector under the circumstances would be inappropriate. If a thrown object spins as it flies through the air, different points of it have different velocities; one can not free these velocities and transfer them from point to point and still describe the motion correctly.

Exercise 4.13 What is the resultant of a velocity of 2 ft./sec. due east and a velocity of $2\sqrt{2}$ ft./sec. northwest? [Note that the wording of this exercise lets it pertain to the definition of velocity as the time rate of change of displacement.]

Exercise 4.14 A certain boat of negligible length has a maximum speed of 4 yds./sec. in still water. The water in a straight canal, 100 yds. wide, flows at 3 yds./sec. If the boat goes at maximum speed while pointing perpendicularly to the bank, what is its speed relative to the bank? How long does it take to cross the canal? [The answer is neither $33\frac{1}{3}$ secs.

*The unpleasant aspects of average velocity are not exorcized by the moving platform concept.

nor 20 secs.] In what direction should the boat be pointed in order to cross the canal perpendicular to the banks, and how long would it take to cross? [It would take $100/\sqrt{7}$ secs.]

5. ACCELERATION

Acceleration is the rate of change of velocity with respect to time. The awkwardness associated with a changing velocity is compounded when we consider acceleration; but, just as in the case of velocity, when ideas belonging to the calculus are brought in, these awkward aspects no longer obtrude. Suffice it to say here that acceleration is a vector quantity. The *average* acceleration of a particle may be said to be the change in velocity divided by the time taken, the velocity being regarded as a free vector. Thus if a point has a velocity of $15\sqrt{3}$ ft./sec. due east at noon and a velocity of 30 ft./sec. 30° north of east at 5 secs. past noon, the change in its velocity is a velocity of 15 ft./sec. due north, as is easily seen from a figure. Since this change of velocity took place in 5 secs., the average acceleration is 3 ft./sec.^{2} due north; we obtain this by dividing the 15 ft./sec. by 5 secs.

Exercise 5.1 A point changes velocity from 144 ft./sec. due east to 144 ft./sec. due north in 8 secs. What is the average acceleration? [*Ans.* $18\sqrt{2}$ ft./sec.^{2} to the northwest.]

Exercise 5.2 A man has a velocity of 5 ft./sec. due east and an acceleration of 5 ft./sec.^{2} due north. Describe the resultant. [One word suffices.]

Exercise 5.3 A point moves in a circle of radius r with constant speed v. Find its average acceleration for (a) one revolution, (b) half of a revolution, and (c) a quarter of a revolution. [Remember that the instantaneous velocity has the direction of the tangent to the circle at the position of the particle. Remember also that though the speed is constant, the velocity changes because its direction changes. In case (c) the average acceleration comes out to have a magnitude of $2\sqrt{2}\, v^2/\pi r$.]

Exercise 5.4 A point moves in a circle with constant speed. Prove geometrically that the average acceleration between two positions, A and B, of the point has a direction parallel to the bisector of the angle between the radii to A and B.

From Exercise 5.4 we see that, in finding the average acceleration of a point moving in a circle with constant speed, the smaller we take the interval of time, the closer together will be the two points, A and B, and the closer will the direction of the average acceleration be to the directions of the radii to A and B. When the time interval is so small that these radii are close to being coincident, the direction of the average acceleration will also be close to being coincident with them. It will come as no great surprise, then, that when one applies ideas belonging to the calculus one finds that the *instantaneous* acceleration at the instant when the point is at A lies along the radius to A and points towards the center of the circle. If the speed were not constant, the instantaneous acceleration would, in general, not lie along the radius.

6. ELEMENTARY STATICS IN TWO DIMENSIONS

If a body placed at rest* remains at rest, it is said to be in *equilibrium*, and the forces acting on it are also said to be in equilibrium. In *statics* we study the conditions under which bodies and forces are in equilibrium.

If a body is so small that we can neglect its size and obtain satisfactory results by treating it mathematically as a point having mass, we call it a particle. (In some investigations quite large bodies—stars, for example—are treated as particles.) According to Newtonian dynamics, a particle of mass m acted on by forces having a resultant $\mathbf{F}$ will undergo an acceleration $\mathbf{a}$ where

$$\mathbf{F} = m\mathbf{a}. \tag{6.1}$$

For a particle to be in equilibrium, it must be unaccelerated, and therefore, by Equation (6.1), the resultant of the forces acting on it must be zero.

If a particle is in equilibrium under the influence of three forces, the forces must be coplanar. This is easily proved. Denote the forces by $\mathbf{F}_1$, $\mathbf{F}_2$, $\mathbf{F}_3$, and let $\mathbf{R}$ be the resultant of $\mathbf{F}_2$ and $\mathbf{F}_3$. Then the three forces are equivalent to $\mathbf{F}_1$ and $\mathbf{R}$. For equilibrium, these two forces must have zero resultant. So $\mathbf{R} = -\mathbf{F}_1$. But the parallelogram construction ensures that $\mathbf{R}$, $\mathbf{F}_2$, and $\mathbf{F}_3$ are coplanar. Therefore $\mathbf{F}_1$, $\mathbf{F}_2$, and $\mathbf{F}_3$ must be too.

Exercise 6.1 A particle is acted on by three forces. Prove that if arrow-headed line segments representing, in the usual way, their magnitudes and directions (but not necessarily their locations) can be appropriately arranged to form a triangle, the particle is in equilibrium. Also prove the converse.

Consider now a rigid body that is too large to be treated as a particle. If

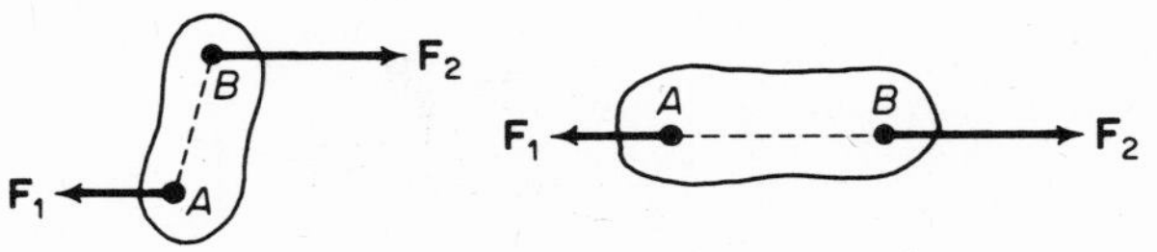

Figure 6.1

it is acted on at points A and B by two parallel forces $\mathbf{F}_1$ and $\mathbf{F}_2$ pointing in opposite directions as shown on the left in Figure 6.1, experiments show that it will be apt to turn and, if friction is present (but not in excessive amounts),

*Let us not ask awkward questions here about the word "rest."

it will take up the final position shown on the right,* with the two forces acting along a common line; and if $\mathbf{F}_1$ and $\mathbf{F}_2$ have equal magnitudes the forces will then be in equilibrium.

From such experiments we infer two things. The first is that a rigid body can transmit the effect of a force unchanged from its point of application to any other point in the body that lies on the line along which the force acts. Because force is a vector quantity that has a definite point of application, it is often referred to as a *bound* vector (a term we have already been using) to distinguish it from a free vector. But when a force acts on a rigid body in equilibrium, its point of application can, in a certain sense, be thought of as free to move along the line of action of the force to another position within the body. Therefore, it is sometimes referred to as a *sliding* vector. Note, though, that if on the left in Figure 6.1 we moved the point of application of the force $\mathbf{F}_1$ from A to another point A' in the body lying on the line of action of A, the body would end up on the right in a position having $A'B$ instead of AB lined up with $\mathbf{F}_1$ and $\mathbf{F}_2$; this position would not be the same as the one illustrated. There is danger, therefore, in thinking of forces as other than bound vectors, though the presence of danger need not prevent us from thinking of them as sliding vectors in appropriate circumstances, such as when a rigid body is held immovable.

The second thing we infer from these experiments is that the conditions for the equilibrium of a rigid body involve the locations of the forces in a significant way, since even if $\mathbf{F}_1$ and $\mathbf{F}_2$ had equal magnitudes, the rigid body would not be in equilibrium when it was in the position on the left, though it would be when in the position on the right.

Two conditions must be fulfilled by the forces acting on a rigid body to produce equilibrium. They are consequences of Equation (6.1), but we shall not give their derivation here. *One condition of equilibrium is that if the forces acting on the body are treated as free vectors their resultant must be zero*—just as if they were all acting on a particle. This condition ensures that the body has no overall translational acceleration. But it must be supplemented by another condition since the forces may still tend to twist the body.

Consider the simple case of a seesaw of negligible mass, as shown, with a boy of weight 75 lbs. at B, x ft. from O, and a man of weight 150 lbs. at M

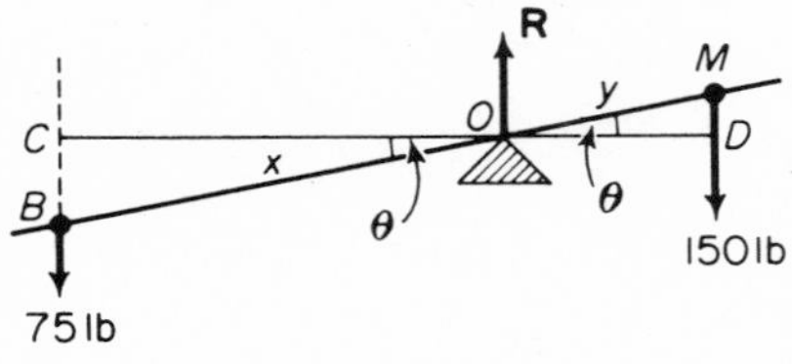

Figure 6.2

*You may think friction is unnecessary. But the situation is not the same as it would be if we were pulling on strings attached to A and B. Can you see why not? The point is a subtle one.

y ft. from O. The turning effect, or *moment*, of the boy's weight is counterclockwise, and it is measured by the product of his weight and the perpendicular distance OC from O to the line of action of the weight. It is therefore $75x \cos \theta$, where θ is as shown. Similarly the turning effect of the man's weight is $150y \cos \theta$, the effect being clockwise. For equilibrium, the clockwise and counterclockwise turning effects must balance. So

$$75x \cos \theta = 150y \cos \theta, \tag{6.2}$$

from which we see that $x = 2y$. Thus, the boy balances the man if he sits twice as far as the man does from the point of support; and the balance then holds for all values of θ.

By regarding counterclockwise moments as positive and clockwise moments as negative, we can rewrite Equation (6.2) in the form:

$$75x \cos \theta + (-\ 150y \cos \theta) = 0. \tag{6.3}$$

It then exemplifies *the second condition for the equilibrium of a rigid body: the total moment of the forces acting on the body must be zero.* [All moments must be about the same point, but this point can be anywhere.] For simplicity we are confining ourselves here to situations in which all the forces lie in a plane. The two conditions of equilibrium, asserted here without proof, hold for the general case; we shall discuss this case when we have developed the necessary vectorial mathematics.

Note that the weights of the boy and the man add up to 225 lbs. so that, at first sight, it seems as if the first condition of equilibrium is not satisfied. But there is a third force acting on the seesaw, namely the reaction on it of the fulcrum at O. (We are assuming that the mass of the seesaw is negligible.) Denote the reaction by $\mathbf{R}$, and its magnitude by R. Then the first condition tells us that $\mathbf{R}$ is vertical, and

$$R - 75 - 150 = 0$$

so that $R = 225$ lbs.

Exercise 6.2 Show that if we took moments about B instead of O the total moment would still be zero. [Note that $\mathbf{R}$ will now have a nonzero moment. Its moment about O is zero, so it would not have made any difference to Equation (6.2) or (6.3), even if we had thought of it at the time.]

Exercise 6.3 Like Exercise 6.2, but taking moments about M.

Exercise 6.4 Prove that if a rigid body is in equilibrium under the influence of three nonparallel coplanar forces, the lines of action of these three forces must meet in a point. [Take moments about the point of intersection of two of these lines of action.]

Exercise 6.5 $ABCD$ is a rigid square of side a. Force $\mathbf{F}_1$ acts at B in the direction from A to B, and force $\mathbf{F}_2$, of equal magnitude, acts at C in the direction from B to C. Find the magnitude, direction, and location of the single additional force that would maintain the square in equilib-

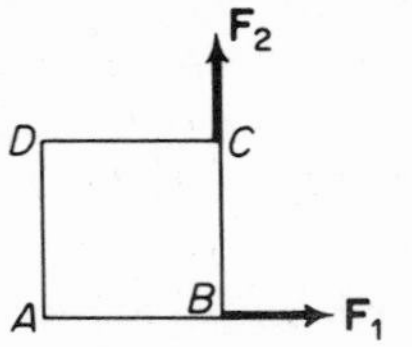

rium. [Use Exercise 6.4.] Verify that the total moment of the three forces about D is zero.

Exercise 6.6 If n parallel coplanar forces acting on a rigid body have zero total moment about a point O in their plane, prove that they do not have zero total moment about every other point in their plane unless they are in equilibrium. [Let the forces have magnitudes $\mathbf{F}_1$, $\mathbf{F}_2$, $\ldots$, $\mathbf{F}_n$ and be at distances $x_1, x_2, \ldots, x_n$ from O. Then $x_1F_1 + x_2F_2 + \ldots + x_nF_n = 0$. But $(x_1 + a)F_1 + (x_2 + a)F_2 + \ldots + (x_n + a)F_n$ will not, in general, be zero.]

7. COUPLES

Consider two parallel forces $\mathbf{F}_1$ and $\mathbf{F}_2$ acting on a rigid body at points A and B as in Figure 7.1, *the forces having equal magnitudes, F, and opposite directions*. Let their distances apart be a. Because the magnitudes of the forces

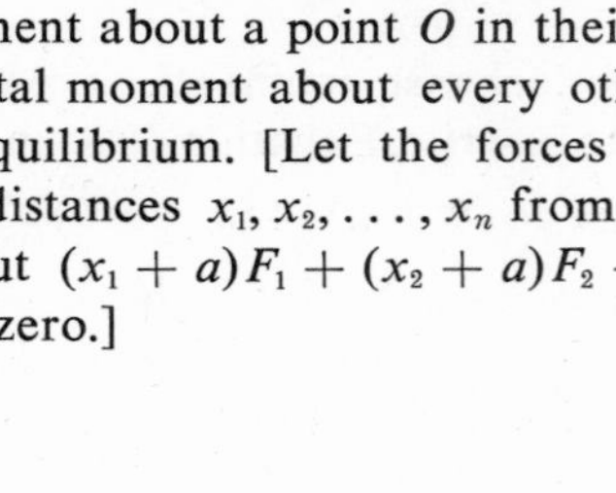

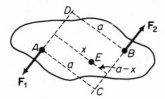

Figure 7.1

are equal, the first condition of equilibrium is satisfied since, when treated as free vectors, $\mathbf{F}_1$ and $\mathbf{F}_2$ have zero resultant. The second condition is not satisfied, though. The forces do not have zero total moment. They tend to turn the body. If we take moments about A, we obtain the values 0 and aF for a total of aF. If we take moments about B we obtain aF and 0, also yielding a total of aF. If we take moments about a point E, in the plane containing the forces, that is distant x from the line of action of F_1 and thus $a - x$ from that of F_2, we obtain $xF + (a - x)F$ which gives the same total, aF, as before.

A pair of parallel forces of equal magnitudes and opposite directions constitutes a *couple*. The magnitude of the moment of a couple is measured by the product of the magnitude of either force and the perpendicular distance between their lines of action. Thus the two forces in Figure 7.1 constitute a couple of moment aF acting counterclockwise. Usually the total moment of a system of forces depends on the position of the point about which the moments are taken. With a couple, though, as we have seen, the moment does not change when the point is changed. Therefore there is no need to specify a point when talking about the moment of a couple.

Suppose a force $\mathbf{F}_1$ of magnitude F acts on a rigid body at point A, as in Figure 7.2. At point B, let us introduce two self-cancelling forces $\mathbf{F}_2$ and $\mathbf{F}_3$

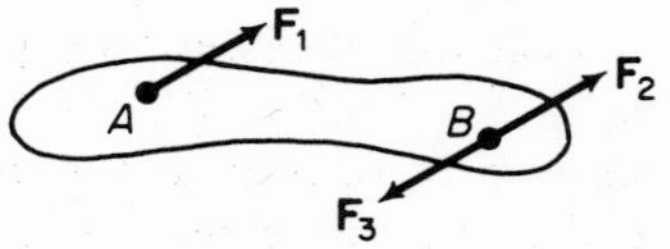

Figure 7.2

parallel to $\mathbf{F}_1$ and having the same magnitude F. Now let us regroup these three forces in our minds: let us think of $\mathbf{F}_1$ and $\mathbf{F}_3$ as forming a couple, and $\mathbf{F}_2$ as standing apart. Then we see that the single force $\mathbf{F}_1$ at A is equivalent to the combination of the single parallel force $\mathbf{F}_2$ of equal magnitude acting at B and the couple formed by $\mathbf{F}_1$ and $\mathbf{F}_3$.

In effect, then, when we move a force to a different line of action (parallel to the original one), we automatically introduce a couple.

Exersise 7.1 In Figure 7.2, if the forces make an angle θ with the line AB, and the distance AB is a, what is the moment of the couple? [*Ans.* $aF \sin \theta$.]

Exercise 7.2 A, B, C, and D are the vertices of a square of side a. A force of magnitude 10 lbs. acts at A and points in the direction $\overrightarrow{AB}$. What couple would be introduced if the force were moved parallel to itself so as to act (a) at B, (b) at C, and (c) at D? [*Ans.* 0, $-10a$, $-10a$.]

Exercise 7.3 A force of magnitude F lbs. pointing in the positive x-direction acts at the origin. A couple in the xy-plane has a moment of G ft. lbs. Where in the xy-plane could the point of application of the force be moved to in order to yield a total couple of H ft. lbs.?

8. THE PROBLEM OF LOCATION. VECTOR FIELDS

The problem of the location of vectors is a vexing one for which there seems to be no wholly satisfactary elementary solution. *The easy way out is to ignore the matter, or to say that such an entity as a force is more than a vector, being a vector equipped with the additional, nonvectorial attribute of location. The purely vectorial aspect of such an entity—its vector, so to speak —is then regarded as a free vector, all vectors being taken to be free vectors.*

There is something highly attractive about this approach. It makes for a neat mathematical theory of vectors. But we really do not understand vectors until we grapple with the problem of location, and ultimately realize that we do not understand it. In this book, therefore, we shall continue to look into the awkward aspects of this problem. The reader who feels that he is uninterested in the problem of location is invited, at any stage in this book, to make the ultimate (or seemingly ultimate) abstraction of denying vectors location and then to ignore all further mentions of the problem. If he does this he will be happier than those who try to face the issue. But he will understand vectors less intimately in the end.

Let us recall the discussion of velocity as the rate of change of displacement with respect to time. Since displacement is a free vector, we at first thought that velocity must be too. But then we thought of the velocity of a particle and felt that this should be located at the particle. And after that, we thought of the velocity of the wind in a storm and realized that there was a different velocity vector at each point.

There are many situations analogous to that of the wind in a storm. The force exerted by a given magnet on another magnet, for instance, is different at different locations of the other magnet. The force exerted by an electric charge on another charge stationary with respect to it also depends on the location. When we have such a situation—an enormous number of vectors, one at each place—we say we have a *vector field.* Mathematically, we would say that there were infinitely many vectors, one at each point. Evidently, in a nonuniform field, we can not switch vectors around to different locations without altering the field. In this sense, the vectors of a vector field have to be considered bound vectors.

By a process of abstraction similar to that that led us from shifts to displacements, we can imagine free vectors associated with the vectors of a field. But then we wonder how much it will profit us to do so. For in a field of force, for example, the force at P does not combine physically by the parallelogram law with the force at a different point Q.

Nevertheless we can ask what is the difference of these two forces in magnitude and direction. And in answering we could go off into a margin and work the problem out, treating the two forces as free vectors and moving them to a common starting point. In working in the margin in this way, we would be working with what the mathematicians call a *linear vector space.* When dealing with forces, we can work in one linear vector space. When dealing with, say, displacements, we can work in another. By judiciously using different linear vector spaces for different situations, we can make the structures of all the linear vector spaces the same, and say that in a *given* linear vector space not only do all vectors have a common starting point, but *every* vector combines with *every other* vector therein according to the parallelogram law.

Pure mathematicians often prefer to start by *defining* vectors as abstract elements in a linear vector space that obey certain rules laid down as axioms. These axioms, indeed, simultaneously define the vectors and the vector space that they inhabit. Often pure mathematicians think of vectors in a vector space as "ordered sets of numbers," by which they mean unpictorial entities like (1, 9, 1, $\frac{1}{2}$) that are counted as different from, say, (9, 1, 1, $\frac{1}{2}$), the amount of numbers in each ordered set depending on the dimensionality of the vector space. By taking this abstract stance, they gain enormously in precision and elegance and power—as generally happens when good mathematicians make abstractions. But the person who studies vectors only as a branch of abstract algebra, regarding them solely as elements in a vector space, obtains the precision and elegance and power at a price. For they come to him too patly for him to realize their worth. He gains no inkling of the motives that led to the choice of just these axioms and abstractions rather than others, and he is apt not to realize how ugly are the seams that join such neat algebraic abstractions to their applications—even to applications to other branches of mathematics such as geometry.

Note, for example, that in asking about the difference of the two forces at P and Q we were not being as reasonable as we thought at the time. We were assuming not only that such a comparison could be made, but also that it could be made in a unique way. That sounds innocent enough. But in effect we were assuming the validity of Euclid's axiom of parallels (among other things) and these days we all know that this axiom can be dispensed with. To pursue this particular aspect of the matter further would be outside the scope of this book. We have pushed it this far in order to show that the problem is not as simple as it sometimes seems.

3

VECTOR ALGEBRA

1. COMPONENTS

Let **V** be a vector starting at a point O. Take any plane containing **V**, and in it draw any two noncoincident lines, $A'A$ and $B'B$, passing through O. Then we can always find two vectors, **X** and **Y**, lying respectively along these

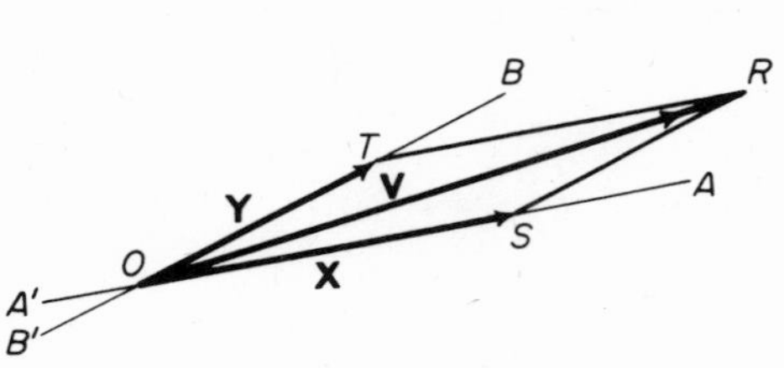

Figure 1.1

two lines, such that **X** and **Y** are together equivalent to **V** —— that is, such that $\mathbf{X} + \mathbf{Y} = \mathbf{V}$. Moreover, the vectors **X** and **Y** are uniquely determined by **V** and the two lines. For, through the end R of **V** we can draw lines RT and RS respectively parallel to $A'A$ and $B'B$, intersecting those lines at S and T respectively. Then $OSRT$ is a parallelogram. Therefore, the vectors represented by $\overrightarrow{OS}$ and $\overrightarrow{OT}$ are uniquely the **X** and **Y** we seek.

Exercise 1.1 Prove the uniqueness of **X** and **Y**.

Let $\mathbf{e}_x$ and $\mathbf{e}_y$ be nonzero vectors starting at O and lying respectively along the lines of action of **X** and **Y**. Denote the ratio of the magnitude of **X** to that of $\mathbf{e}_x$ by V_x, taking V_x to be positive if **X** and $\mathbf{e}_x$ have the same direction, and negative if they have opposite directions. Similarly, denote the ratio of the magnitude of **Y** to that of $\mathbf{e}_y$ by V_y, these quantities, V_x and V_y, being, of course, not vectors. Then we can write:

$$\mathbf{X} = V_x \mathbf{e}_x \,, \qquad \mathbf{Y} = V_y \mathbf{e}_y \,. \tag{1.1}$$

V_x and V_y are called the *components* of the vector **V** relative to (or with respect to, or in) the *frame of reference* defined by $\mathbf{e}_x$ and $\mathbf{e}_y$. The point O is called the *origin* of the frame of reference, and $\mathbf{e}_x$, $\mathbf{e}_y$ its *base vectors.* Some books use the word components for the vectors **X** and **Y**, and then fail to make a sharp verbal distinction between **X**, **Y** and V_x, V_y. To avoid confusion, we shall refer to **X** and **Y** as *component vectors* of **V**.

Exercise 1.2 A vector of magnitude 144 makes 45° with each of two perpendicular lines. What are its component vectors along these lines? [There are four possible answers to the question as worded.]

Exercise 1.3 In Exercise 1.2, if $\mathbf{e}_x$ and $\mathbf{e}_y$ lie along the perpendicular lines, and $\mathbf{e}_x$ has a magnitude of 4 and $\mathbf{e}_y$ a magnitude of 6, what are the components of the vector relative to the reference frame defined by the base vectors $\mathbf{e}_x$ and $\mathbf{e}_y$? [*Ans.* $\pm\, 18\sqrt{2}$, $\pm\, 12\sqrt{2}$.]

Exercise 1.4 If $\mathbf{e}_x$ and $\mathbf{e}_y$ have unit magnitude and are perpendicular, what are the components of a vector of magnitude h pointing along the positive direction of $\mathbf{e}_x$? Would the components be different if $\mathbf{e}_y$ were not perpendicular to $\mathbf{e}_x$? [In situations of this sort we shall assume that the vectors have the same starting point unless they are free vectors, in which case the assumption is unnecessary.]

Exercise 1.5 If $\mathbf{e}_x$ has a fixed direction but $\mathbf{e}_y$ a varying one, is V_x constant or not?

Exercise 1.6 Find the component vectors of a vector of magnitude 10 pointing 30° north of east relative to (a) the east and north directions, (b) the east and northwest directions, and (c) the east direction and the direction 30° north of east.

Exercise 1.7 In Exercise 1.6, find the component of the given vector relative to the reference frame $\mathbf{e}_x$, $\mathbf{e}_y$, if $\mathbf{e}_x$ has magnitude 2 and $\mathbf{e}_y$ magnitude 1, and if, in each part, $\mathbf{e}_x$ points to the east while $\mathbf{e}_y$ points in the second direction mentioned. [*Ans.* (b) $5(\sqrt{3} + 1)/2$, $5\sqrt{2}$.]

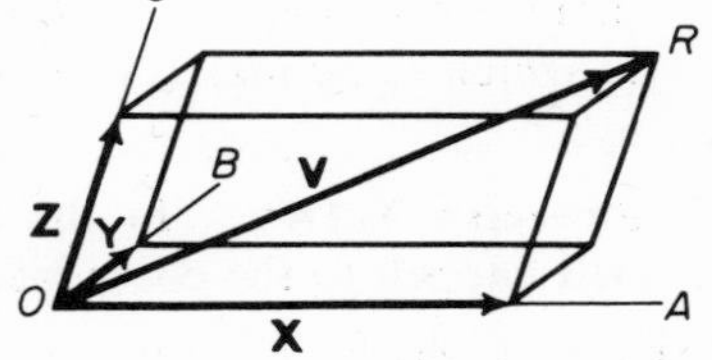

Figure 1.2

If, in Figure 1.1, the vector V did not lie in the plane of the lines $A'A$ and $B'B$, we could not have constructed the parallelogram. But if we take *three* lines OA, OB, and OC that do not lie in a plane, we can always* find, along the respective lines, vectors **X**, **Y**, and **Z** that are together equivalent to **V**; these three vectors are uniquely determined by **V** and the lines. The method is to construct a parallelepiped with edges along and parallel to the three chosen lines OA, OB, and OC, as in Figure 1.2.

Exercise 1.8 Explain how to construct the parallelepiped in Figure 1.2 by passing appropriate planes through R.

Exercise 1.9 Prove that $\mathbf{X} + \mathbf{Y} + \mathbf{Z} = \mathbf{V}$ in Figure 1.2 (a) by first combining **X** and **Y** and combining their resultant with **Z**; (b) by first combining **Y** and **Z**; (c) by first combining **Z** and **X**; and (d) by using the end-to-end method of finding the resultant of several vectors.

If we introduce three nonzero base vectors $\mathbf{e}_x$, $\mathbf{e}_y$, $\mathbf{e}_z$ along OA, OB, and OC, respectively, we can write:

$$\mathbf{X} = V_x\mathbf{e}_x, \qquad \mathbf{Y} = V_y\mathbf{e}_y, \qquad \mathbf{Z} = V_z\mathbf{e}_z, \tag{1.2}$$

the quantities V_x, V_y, and V_z being the components of **V** with respect to the reference frame defined by $\mathbf{e}_x$, $\mathbf{e}_y$, and $\mathbf{e}_z$. Then, since $\mathbf{V} = \mathbf{X} + \mathbf{Y} + \mathbf{Z}$, we have:

$$\mathbf{V} = V_x\mathbf{e}_x + V_y\mathbf{e}_y + V_z\mathbf{e}_z. \tag{1.3}$$

Exercise 1.10 In two dimensions, if $\mathbf{U} = \mathbf{U}_x\mathbf{e}_x + \mathbf{U}_y\mathbf{e}_y$ and $\mathbf{V} = V_x\mathbf{e}_x + V_y\mathbf{e}_y$, show by means of a diagram that $\mathbf{U} + \mathbf{V} = (U_x + V_x)\mathbf{e}_x + (U_y + V_y)\mathbf{e}_y$ and $\mathbf{U} - \mathbf{V} = (U_x - V_x)\mathbf{e}_x + (U_y - V_y)\mathbf{e}_y$. [Note how neatly the symbols, + and −, applied to vectors turn out to be related to the algebraic symbols, + and −, applied to their components.]

Exercise 1.11 Prove the relations in Exercise 1.10 algebraically by noting that $\mathbf{U} + \mathbf{V}$ is really the sum of four vectors $U_x\mathbf{e}_x$, $U_y\mathbf{e}_y$, $V_x\mathbf{e}_x$, and $V_y\mathbf{e}_y$, adding the first and third, then the second and fourth, and combining the results.

Exercise 1.12 Relative to $\mathbf{e}_x$ and $\mathbf{e}_y$, let **U** have components U_x and U_y, let **V** have components V_x and V_y, and let **W** have components W_x and W_y. What are the components of $\mathbf{U} + \mathbf{V} - \mathbf{W}$?

Exercise 1.13 In Exercise 1.12, what must be true of the components of **U**, **V**, and **W** if $\mathbf{U} + \mathbf{V} - \mathbf{W}$ (a) points in the $\mathbf{e}_x$ direction, (b) points in the negative $\mathbf{e}_y$ direction (i. e., in the direction opposite to that in which $\mathbf{e}_y$ points), (c) lies along the direction of the resultant of $\mathbf{e}_x$ and $\mathbf{e}_y$?

Exercise 1.14 In the situation epitomized in Equation (1.3), what will happen to the components of **V** if the magnitudes of the base vectors

*Beware of the word "always." It is almost "always" wrong. What if we were discussing three lines in four dimensions, for example?

$\mathbf{e}_x$, $\mathbf{e}_y$, and $\mathbf{e}_z$ are increased to 5 times their present values? [Note that the components become smaller, not larger.]

Exercise 1.15 In Equation (1.3) what new magnitudes for $\mathbf{e}_x$, $\mathbf{e}_y$, and $\mathbf{e}_z$ would make the components of $\mathbf{V}$ all equal to 1? Are there exceptional cases?

Exercise 1.16 What are the components of $\mathbf{e}_x$, $\mathbf{e}_y$, and $\mathbf{e}_z$ respectively in the reference frame defined by $\mathbf{e}_x$, $\mathbf{e}_y$, and $\mathbf{e}_z$?

Exercise 1.17 If $\mathbf{U} = U_x\mathbf{e}_x + U_y\mathbf{e}_y + U_z\mathbf{e}_z$ and $\mathbf{V} = V_x\mathbf{e}_x + V_y\mathbf{e}_y + V_z\mathbf{e}_z$, show that the components of $a\mathbf{U} \pm b\mathbf{V}$ are $aU_x \pm bV_x$, etc., a and b being numbers.

Exercise 1.18 If, relative to $\mathbf{e}_x$, $\mathbf{e}_y$, and $\mathbf{e}_z$, $\mathbf{U}$ has components $(6, 2, -4)$, what can you say about the components of $\mathbf{V}$ (a) if $\mathbf{U} + 2\mathbf{V}$ lies along the $\mathbf{e}_x$ direction? (b) if $3\mathbf{U} - \mathbf{V}$ lies in the plane defined by $\mathbf{e}_y$ and $\mathbf{e}_z$? (c) if $\mathbf{U} + \mathbf{V}$ is the same as $6\mathbf{e}_x + 2\mathbf{e}_y - 4\mathbf{e}_z$? (d) if $\mathbf{e}_x + \mathbf{U} = 3\mathbf{e}_y + \mathbf{V}$? [*Ans.* (a) Since $\mathbf{e}_x$ has components $(1, 0, 0)$, we must have $6 + 2V_x =$ some constant, $2 + 2V_y = 0$, $-4 + 2V_z = 0$. So we can say that $V_y = -1$, $V_z = 2$.]

Exercise 1.19 Relative to $\mathbf{e}_x$, $\mathbf{e}_y$, and $\mathbf{e}_z$, the velocity of an airplane has components (100, 150, 20) and the wind velocity has components $(30, -20, 0)$. What are the components of the velocity with which the wind passes the plane? [*Ans.* $(30 - 100, -20 - 150, 0 - 20)$, or $(-70, -170, -20)$, just like that! Note how much easier it is here to work with components than with arrow-headed line segments and three-dimensional diagrams.]

Exercise 1.20 A particle in equilibrium is acted on by three forces, two of which have components $(6, 5, -2)$ and $(3, -10, 8)$ respectively, relative to a particular reference frame. What are the components of the third force? [*Ans.* $(-9, 5, -6)$.]

2. UNIT ORTHOGONAL TRIADS

The formidable title of this section has to do with something that is simpler than what was studied in the preceding section, being a special case of it.

If we know the components of a vector with respect to a reference frame, we know the vector, for it is given by Equation (1.3). Theoretically, then, we ought to be able to calculate its magnitude once we know its components in a given reference frame. And indeed we can. But when the reference frame is a general one of the type considered in the preceding section, the formula is rather complicated. Consider, for example, the two-dimensional case, with the reference vectors $\mathbf{e}_x$ and $\mathbf{e}_y$ making an angle θ with each other. If the components of $\mathbf{V}$ are V_x and V_y, and the magnitudes of $\mathbf{e}_x$ and $\mathbf{e}_y$ are e_x and e_y, then the lines OS and OT in Figure 2.1 are respectively of length $V_x e_x$ and $V_y e_y$. In triangle OSR, SR has the length of OT, namely $V_y e_y$, and angle OSR is $180° - \theta$. So, by the law of cosines, since $\cos(180° - \theta) = -\cos\theta$, we have:

$$V^2 = V_x^2 e_x^2 + V_y^2 e_y^2 + 2V_x e_x V_y e_y \cos\theta, \tag{2.1}$$

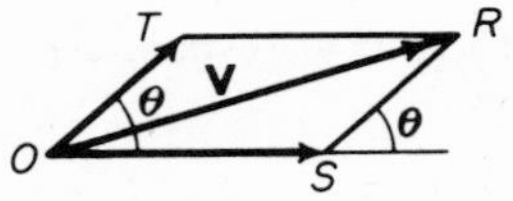

Figure 2.1

a none-too-pleasant formula even without our taking the square roots of both sides. And this is just for the two-dimensional case.

In many situations, of which the preceding is one, the work is significantly simplified if we use a special type of reference frame, though the simplification is obtained at a price: loss of generality and of depth of understanding.

The idea is to use reference frames in which $\mathbf{e}_x$, $\mathbf{e}_y$, and $\mathbf{e}_z$ are mutually perpendicular and of unit magnitude; hence the title of this section. It is customary to denote the vectors $\mathbf{e}_x$, $\mathbf{e}_y$, and $\mathbf{e}_z$ of such a unit orthogonal reference triad by the special symbols **i**, **j**, and **k**. Note that **i** does not stand for $\sqrt{-1}$ here. For one thing, it is printed in boldface type.

The parallelepiped in Figure 1.2 now becomes rectangular, as in Figure 2.2. [Note the change in letters.] And instead of Equation (1.3) we have:

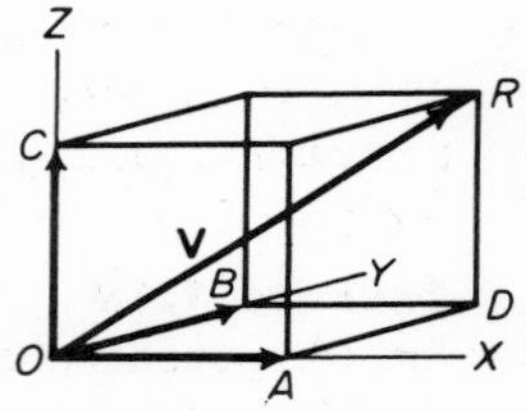

Figure 2.2

$$\mathbf{V} = V_x\mathbf{i} + V_y\mathbf{j} + V_z\mathbf{k}. \tag{2.2}$$

What is the magnitude of **V** in terms of V_x, V_y, and V_z? If **V** is represented by $\overrightarrow{OR}$ in Figure 2.2, Equation (2.2) tells us that

$$OA = V_x, \qquad OB = V_y, \qquad OC = V_z, \tag{2.3}$$

since the magnitudes of **i**, **j**, and **k** are all unity. [But we shall have to return to this in the next chapter.] Applying Pythagoras' theorem to the right triangle OAD, we have $OD^2 = OA^2 + AD^2$. And applying it to the right triangle ODR, we have $OR^2 = OD^2 + DR^2$. So $OR^2 = OA^2 + AD^2 + DR^2 = OA^2 + OB^2 + OC^2$. But OR is the magnitude of **V**. Therefore, by Equation (2.3),

$$V^2 = V_x^2 + V_y^2 + V_z^2, \tag{2.4}$$

from which we obtain

$$V = \sqrt{V_x^2 + V_y^2 + V_z^2}. \tag{2.5}$$

Since the magnitude is always counted as non-negative, we do not use a $\pm$ sign in Equation (2.5).

Exercise 2.1 A vector has components (1, 1, 1) relative to **i**, **j**, and **k**. What is its magnitude? Describe as best you can its direction in relation to **i**, **j**, and **k**.

Exercise 2.2 Like Exercise 2.1 for a vector having components (1, 1, $-$ 1).

Exercise 2.3 What are the magnitudes of the vectors having the following components relative to **i**, **j**, and **k**? (a) (1, 2, 2); (b) (− 4, − 4, 7); (c) ($\sqrt{3}$, $\sqrt{7}$, − $\sqrt{6}$); (d) (10, − 20, − 30); (e) (V_x, V_y, 0).

Exercise 2.4 Relative to a unit orthogonal triad, a vector **U** has components (5, 12, 5) and a vector **V** has components (4, − 3, z). What can you say about z if **U** and **V** have equal magnitudes?

Exercise 2.5 If **U** and **V** have components (U_x, U_y, U_z) and (V_x, V_y, V_z) relative to **i**, **j**, and **k**, what are the magnitudes of **U** + **V** and **U** − **V**?

Exercise 2.6 A particle is acted on by two forces **F** and **F′** having components (F_x, F_y, F_z) and (F'_x, F'_y, F'_z) relative to **i**, **j**, and **k**. What are the components and magnitude of the force that will keep the particle in equilibrium?

Exercise 2.7 What is the locus of the tip of a vector of fixed magnitude r and fixed initial point O? If the components of the vector relative to **i**, **j**, and **k** are (x, y, z) what equation must these quantities satisfy?

For given **i** and **j**, we can take **k** in either of the two opposite directions perpendicular to the plane of **i** and **j**, as shown in Figure 2.3. The two configurations (a) and (b) are distinct. We can not maneuver one of them as a rigid body so as to make it coincide with the other. We therefore give the configurations different names; we refer to (a) as a *right-handed system* and to (b) as a *left-handed system*.

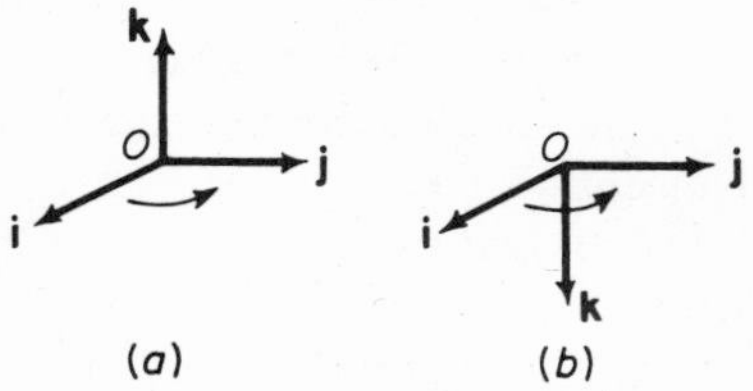

Figure 2.3

Imagine a right-handed corkscrew pointing along the **k**-direction in the right-handed system in (a). If we twist the handle as if we were trying to make **i** take up the position now occupied by **j** (via the 90° route, not the 270° one!) the corkscrew will move in the direction in which **k** points. In the left-handed system (b) it will move in the direction opposite to that in which **k** points.

Exercise 2.8 Verify that the preceding paragraph will remain valid if we replace **i**, **j**, and **k** by **j**, **k**, and **i** respectively, or by **k**, **i**, and **j** respectively.

Exercise 2.9 In Figure 2.2, do the lines OA, OB, and OC form a right-handed or a left-handed system? What if we took them in the order OB, OC, and OA? What if we took them in the order OB, OA, and OC? [*Ans.* right-handed; right-handed; left-handed.]

Exercise 2.10 Starting with a right-handed system, what does it become if we reverse the direction of one axis? Of two? Of three?

Exercise 2.11 Give a definition of right-handedness that would apply to a general reference frame defined by $\mathbf{e}_x$, $\mathbf{e}_y$, and $\mathbf{e}_z$ in that order [Note the importance of the words *in that order*. We usually take them for granted without mentioning them. The definition is a simple generalization of that for the orthogonal case; but one must be careful to specify that, for example, the rotation of $\mathbf{e}_x$ towards $\mathbf{e}_y$ is via the shorter route. What is the maximum angle one could permit in this connection?]

3. POSITION VECTORS

Let the period at the end of this sentence represent a point P.

Where is the point P? We could say it is right there, at the end of the sentence. But where is the sentence? On page 40 of a book? Then where is the book? On a table in a certain room on the earth? Then where is the earth?

After pushing this silent dialogue with ourselves a little further, we begin to realize that the concept of "where" is fundamentally a puzzling one.

But suppose we erect a frame of reference by means of three base vectors $\mathbf{e}_x$, $\mathbf{e}_y$, and $\mathbf{e}_z$. Then, without knowing *where* this frame of reference is in any deep sense of the word, we can nevertheless ask where a point is in relation to the reference frame; and this relative sort of *where* is a far more tractable concept.

To specify the location of a point relative to a frame of reference, it suffices to give the components of the vector that starts at O and ends at the point. For example, in Figure 1.2 the location of the point R relative to the reference frame is given by the components of the vector $\mathbf{V}$ relative to the frame.

Exercise 3.1 Point R is the midpoint of $\mathbf{e}_x$. Denote the vector $\overrightarrow{OR}$ by $\mathbf{V}$. What are the components of $\mathbf{V}$ relative to $\mathbf{e}_x$, $\mathbf{e}_y$, and $\mathbf{e}_z$?

Exercise 3.2 What would the components of the vector $\mathbf{V}$ in Exercise 3.1 become if, keeping the same origin, we rotated to a new reference frame with base vectors $\mathbf{e}'_x$, $\mathbf{e}'_y$, and $\mathbf{e}'_z$ such that $\mathbf{e}'_x = \mathbf{e}_y$, $\mathbf{e}'_y = \mathbf{e}_z$, and $\mathbf{e}'_z = \mathbf{e}_x$? [*Ans.* $(0, 0, \frac{1}{2})$.]

We could dispense with a reference frame, retaining only its origin, O, and specifying the point R by means of the vector $\mathbf{V}$ itself rather than by means of its components relative to some reference frame. Or so it would seem. Indeed, the idea becomes quite attractive when we recall that if we change from one reference frame to another having the same origin, the components of $\mathbf{V}$ change but the vector itself does not.

But what do we mean when we say that the vector $\mathbf{V}$ does not change? Change relative to what? How do we know it isn't whirling around O at an alarming rate? You say you know because you are holding your book steady? Then hurl it into the air, and now try answering the question.

It is clear that when we think we are dispensing with a reference frame we really are not. In doing Exercise 3.2 above, did we so much as pause to ask ourselves what was meant by "the vector $\mathbf{V}$ in Exercise 3.1"? Did we not assume that the meaning was obvious? The meaning is indeed obvious. But let us face what it implies. In thinking of **V** as being the same in Exercises 3.1 and 3.2, we have in mind some master reference frame relative to which **V** is indeed unchanging. It could be the frame $\mathbf{e}_x$, $\mathbf{e}_y$, and $\mathbf{e}_z$, but it need not be; and the chances are that we do not think of it as being that reference frame. However, we do here think of $\mathbf{e}_x$, $\mathbf{e}_y$, and $\mathbf{e}_z$ as being unchanging vectors relative to this master frame, and we think of $\mathbf{e}'_x$, $\mathbf{e}'_y$, and $\mathbf{e}'_z$ as being so too. And if we should have occasion to speak of a *moving* reference frame, we would really mean that it was moving relative to some other frame, whether we mentioned this other frame or not.

Having looked into the situation, we may, for the most part, go on speaking about fixed vectors, fixed points, and the like as we have been doing all along, realizing now that we are really doing so in relation to some mentioned or unmentioned master reference frame.

Given a fixed reference point O, then, we can specify the position of a point P by means of a vector having magnitude and direction represented by the arrow-headed line segment $\overrightarrow{OP}$. This vector is called the *position vector* of P relative to O.

In what sense can we locate a point P relative to a point O by means of a *vector?* In thinking of $\overrightarrow{OP}$ not just as an arrow-headed line segment but as a vector, we commit ourselves to seemingly nonsensical things about the positions of points; for example, that if $OPRQ$ is a parallelogram, the position of P relative to O and the position of Q relative to O are together somehow equivalent to the position of R relative to O. Stated this way, it is indeed nonsense. It makes sense if we regard these positions as displacements, even though they were all conceived as positions relative to the same point O; but it does not make the sort of sense we had in mind when we thought we were specifying the locations of points relative to O. Even so, the idea of representing these positions by means of vectors that we then regard as displacements is a powerful one, as the following exercises will indicate.

Exercise 3.3 If points A and B have position vectors **a** and **b** relative to O, what is the position vector of the mid-point M of AB?

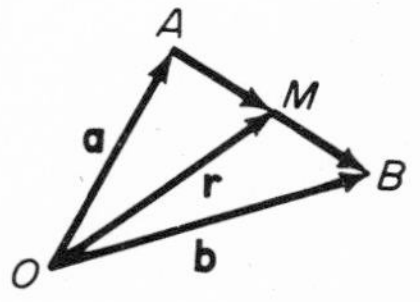

Figure 3.1

Solution Denote the position vector of M by **r**. Then, regarding **a** and **b** as displacements, which are free vectors, we have:

$$\overrightarrow{AM} = \overrightarrow{OM} - \overrightarrow{OA} = \mathbf{r} - \mathbf{a}$$

and

$$\overrightarrow{MB} = \overrightarrow{OB} - \overrightarrow{OM} = \mathbf{b} - \mathbf{r}.$$

But the displacements $\overrightarrow{AM}$ and $\overrightarrow{MB}$ are equal. Therefore,

$$\mathbf{r} - \mathbf{a} = \mathbf{b} - \mathbf{r},$$

from which we find that

$$\mathbf{r} = \frac{1}{2}(\mathbf{a} + \mathbf{b}). \tag{3.1}$$

This relation is called the MID-POINT FORMULA.

Exercise 3.4 Points A_1 and A_2 have position vectors $\mathbf{a}_1$ and $\mathbf{a}_2$ relative to O. A point P on A_1A_2 is such that $A_1P/PA_2 = m_1/m_2$, where m_1 and m_2 are numbers. Show that the position vector, $\mathbf{r}$, of the point P is given by:

$$\mathbf{r} = \frac{m_2\mathbf{a}_1 + m_1\mathbf{a}_2}{m_1 + m_2}. \tag{3.2}$$

[This relation is called the POINT-OF-DIVISION FORMULA.]

Exercise 3.5 Using vectors, prove that the medians of a triangle meet at a point that divides each median in the ratio 2:1 starting from its vertex.

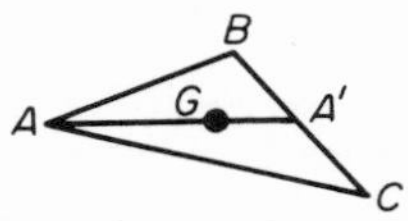

Figure 3.2

Solution Denote the position vectors of the vertices A, B, and C of the triangle by $\mathbf{a}$, $\mathbf{b}$, and $\mathbf{c}$ respectively. Then, by the mid-point formula, the position vector of the mid-point A' of side BC is $\frac{1}{2}(\mathbf{b} + \mathbf{c})$. Let G be the point of AA' such that $AG = 2GA'$, so that $AG{:}GA' = 2{:}1$. Then, by the point-of-division formula, the position vector of G is:

$$\frac{1\mathbf{a} + 2\left[\frac{1}{2}(\mathbf{b} + \mathbf{c})\right]}{3},$$

which is just $\frac{1}{3}(\mathbf{a} + \mathbf{b} + \mathbf{c})$. This quantity is symmetrical in $\mathbf{a}$, $\mathbf{b}$, and $\mathbf{c}$: though we found it by going two-thirds of the way down the median through A, it contains the vector $\mathbf{a}$ on an equal footing with $\mathbf{b}$ and $\mathbf{c}$. Consequently, if we did the corresponding calculations for the other medians they would have to give essentially the same result — if we made no mistakes, or all our mistakes cancelled. Therefore, the point G is common to all three medians.

Exercise 3.6 Do Exercise 3.5 in terms of the median through B.

Exercise 3.7 Using vectors, prove that the line segments joining the mid-points of opposite sides of any quadrilateral, whether plane or skew, bisect each other.

A position vector is a curious thing. It is akin to a displacement, but instead of being free it is tied to a particular origin O. If the position vector of a point with respect to an origin O has the same magnitude and direction as that of P' relative to O', the points P and P' will not coincide unless O and O' do. With O and O' distinct, the position vectors $\overrightarrow{OP}$ and $\overrightarrow{O'P'}$ do not define the same position, though they would be counted as equal vectors if they were displacements. Yet if we think of a position vector as a bound vector starting at O we have to wonder in what sense, for example, the position vectors $\overrightarrow{OA}$ and $\overrightarrow{OM}$ in Figure 3.1 can combine to give a vector $\overrightarrow{AM}$ that not only does not start at O but does not even pass through O. And we may conclude that $\overrightarrow{OM} - \overrightarrow{OA}$ does not yield $\overrightarrow{AM}$ but a vector starting at O having the same magnitude and direction as $\overrightarrow{AM}$. This is awkward, but Exercise 3.3 and others like it can, in fact, be worked out in terms of vectors all of which start at O.

Exercise 3.8 Work out Exercise 3.3 in terms of such vectors. (Note that a crucial step is to require that the vectors defined by $\overrightarrow{OM} - \overrightarrow{OA}$ and $\overrightarrow{OB} - \overrightarrow{OM}$ be identical. Draw the two parallelograms involved.)

Perhaps we find it distasteful to work in this way here in terms of bound vectors all starting at O. But before we decide to reject them, let us consider Figure 3.3. What does it represent? Three guesses: A design with match sticks? A lopsided equation telling that $X = 1$? A preliminary study for a modern work of art? All wrong. It is Figure 3.1 done in terms of free vectors (with letters and arrowheads omitted).

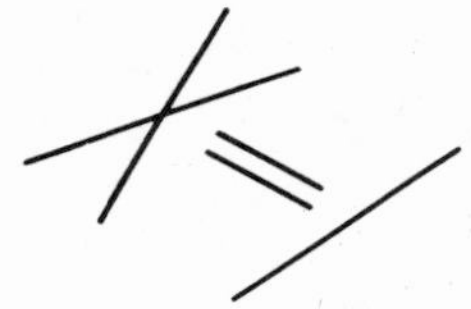

Figure 3.3

When one is dealing with position vectors, there seems to be no way of avoiding aukwardness, except by ignoring it. But that is not a bad method.

Exercise 3.9 It is instructive to try to do Exercise 3.3 solely in terms of shifts, using only relations of the type $OA + AM = OM$. Try this, and note why the attempt does not succeed [For example, AM and MB are not identical shifts, and Equation (3.1) is not applicable to shifts, though it is to displacements corresponding to shifts. One sees from this how powerful is the concept of a vector as compared with that of a shift, even though the shift seems to contain more data of importance.]

Suppose, in Exercise 3.3, we changed from the origin O to a new origin O'. Then all the position vectors would be changed. Yet (relative to our master reference frame) the points A, M, and B would not move, and M would remain the mid-point of the line segment AB. Clearly, the mid-point formula (3.1) will have to hold for the new position vectors as well as for the old. If we are dubious (though the foregoing is really a sufficient proof), we can check very easily. Let the position vector of O' relative to O be $\mathbf{h}$. Then, from Figure 3.4, we see that the old position vector $\mathbf{a}$ of point A is related to its new position vector $\mathbf{a}'$ by

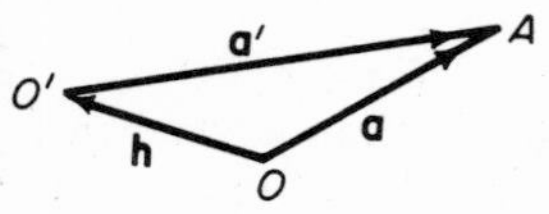

Figure 3.4

$$\mathbf{a} = \mathbf{a}' + \mathbf{h}. \tag{3.3}$$

Similar relations hold for all other position vectors. Let us introduce new

position vectors for old ones in Equation (3.1), namely $\mathbf{r} = \frac{1}{2}(\mathbf{a} + \mathbf{b})$. Then we have

$$\mathbf{r}' + \mathbf{h} = \tfrac{1}{2}\,[(\mathbf{a}' + \mathbf{h}) + (\mathbf{b}' + \mathbf{h})],$$

which reduces to

$$\mathbf{r}' = \tfrac{1}{2}\,(\mathbf{a}' + \mathbf{b}'),$$

as we foretold that it must.

Exercise 3.10 Show by the two methods above that the point-of-division formula (3.2) also holds for new position vectors when the origin is changed.

Exercise 3.11 Like Exercise 3.10 for the formulas for the position vectors of the ultimate points of intersection in Exercises 3.5 and 3.7.

There is a simple theorem that tells us what sort of linear relation between position vectors preserves its form when the origin is changed. Let the relation be:

$$\alpha_1\mathbf{a}_1 + \alpha_2\mathbf{a}_2 + \ldots + \alpha_n\mathbf{a}_n = 0, \tag{3.4}$$

where the **a**'s are position vectors relative to O, and the α's are numbers. Make the change to a new origin O' by means of equations of which Equation (3.3) is a specimen. Then Equation (3.4) becomes:

$$\alpha_1(\mathbf{a}_1' + \mathbf{h}) + \alpha_2(\mathbf{a}_2' + \mathbf{h}) + \ldots + \alpha_n(\mathbf{a}_n' + \mathbf{h}) = 0$$

or

$$\alpha_1\mathbf{a}_1' + \alpha_2\mathbf{a}_2' + \ldots + \alpha_n\mathbf{a}_n' + (\alpha_1 + \alpha_2 + \ldots + \alpha_n)\mathbf{h} = 0,$$

and this will reduce to Equation (3.4), with **a**′'s replacing **a**'s, if and only if

$$\alpha_1 + \alpha_2 + \ldots + \alpha_n = 0. \tag{3.5}$$

Exercise 3.12 Verify that the condition (3.5) is satisfied by Equation (3.1). [Write Equation (3.1) as $\mathbf{r} - \frac{1}{2}\mathbf{a} - \frac{1}{2}\mathbf{b} = 0$ and note that the coefficients $1, -\frac{1}{2}$, and $-\frac{1}{2}$ add up to zero.]

Exercise 3.13 Like Exercise 3.12 for the results of Exercises 3.4, 3.5, and 3.7. [Note that in Figure 3.2 we did not even bother to draw the origin.]

If, without drawing the origin, we can draw a diagram that nevertheless contains all the essential data, the expression of these data in terms of position vectors will retain the same form when the origin is changed. And this will be true even if the relations between the vectors are nonlinear. The reason is so simple as to be almost primitive. The position vectors depend on the origin. If they are used in order to represent a configuration that does not even involve an origin, then they must do so in a way that does not give one particular origin preference over any other. Therefore, the relation between the position vectors must retain the same form when the origin is changed, since otherwise all origins would not enjoy equal status—or perhaps we should say here, lack of status.

Examples of such situations are easy to find. For instance, we can draw a diagram of the fact that M is the mid-point of the line segment AB without needing to draw in an origin. Other such situations have been encountered in Exercises 3.4, 3.5, and 3.7. Yet others are that four given points lie in a plane, or that they lie at the vertices of a regular tetrahedron, or that one of the points is the intersection of the angle bisectors of the triangle formed by the other three. [The vectorial formula for this last would probably be encountered as a formula for the position vector of the point of intersection of the angle bisectors in terms of the position vectors of the vertices of the triangle.]

Exercise 3.14 Show by means of Equation (3.3) that $\overrightarrow{OB} - \overrightarrow{OA} = \overrightarrow{O'B} - \overrightarrow{O'A}$, and therefore, that any vector relationship built up solely of combinations of the form $\overrightarrow{OB} - \overrightarrow{OA}$ will retain its form when the origin is changed. [Note how this is related to the preceding discussion of diagrams in view of the fact that $\overrightarrow{OB} - \overrightarrow{OA} = \overrightarrow{AB}$.]

Exercise 3.15 Show that if $\mathbf{a}_1$, $\mathbf{a}_2$, and $\mathbf{a}_3$ are position vectors and β_{23}, β_{31}, and β_{12} are numbers, the linear relation among differences of $\mathbf{a}$'s,

$$\beta_{23}(\mathbf{a}_2 - \mathbf{a}_3) + \beta_{31}(\mathbf{a}_3 - \mathbf{a}_1) + \beta_{12}(\mathbf{a}_1 - \mathbf{a}_2) = 0,$$

satisfies the condition (3.5) for being independent of the origin.

Exercise 3.16 Extend Exercise 3.15 to the case of n position vectors $\mathbf{a}_1, \mathbf{a}_2, \ldots, \mathbf{a}_n$.

Exercise 3.17 Show that if $\mathbf{a}_1$, $\mathbf{a}_2$, and $\mathbf{a}_3$ are position vectors and the linear relation

$$\alpha_1\mathbf{a}_1 + \alpha_2\mathbf{a}_2 + \alpha_3\mathbf{a}_3 = 0$$

is independent of the origin so that $\alpha_1 + \alpha_2 + \alpha_3 = 0$, then the linear relation can be written as a linear relation among differences of position vectors. [Thus we can rearrange the left-hand side by writing it as $\alpha_1(\mathbf{a}_1 - \mathbf{a}_2) + (\alpha_1 + \alpha_2)\mathbf{a}_2 + \alpha_3\mathbf{a}_3$, which is equal to $\alpha_1(\mathbf{a}_1 - \mathbf{a}_2) + (\alpha_1 + \alpha_2)(\mathbf{a}_2 - \mathbf{a}_3) + (\alpha_1 + \alpha_2 + \alpha_3)\mathbf{a}_3$, and the last term vanishes because of the conditions on the α's. Now work the problem starting with $\mathbf{a}_3$ instead of $\mathbf{a}_1$, and note that the resulting relation has a different form.]

Exercise 3.18 At first sight, it may seem surprising that there should be various ways of expressing a linear relation among position vectors in terms of differences of such vectors, in view of the fact that these differences directly represent line segments in a diagram that does not contain O. To understand what is involved, show that the mid-point formula in Exercise 3.3 can be rewritten in the following three forms, and state their geometric interpretation in terms of line segments involving the points A, M, and B: $(\mathbf{r}-\mathbf{a})+(\mathbf{r}-\mathbf{b})=0$, $(\mathbf{r}-\mathbf{a})-\frac{1}{2}(\mathbf{b}-\mathbf{a})=0$; $(\mathbf{r}-\mathbf{b})-\frac{1}{2}(\mathbf{a}-\mathbf{b})=0$.

Exercise 3.19 Denoting the position vector of the point G in Exercise 3.5 by $\mathbf{g}$, express the relation $\mathbf{g}=\frac{1}{3}(\mathbf{a}+\mathbf{b}+\mathbf{c})$ in a form involving only differences of position vectors, and interpret the result geometrically. [One such form is $(\mathbf{g}-\mathbf{a})+(\mathbf{g}-\mathbf{b})+(\mathbf{g}-\mathbf{c})=0$. This tells us that the vectors represented by $\overrightarrow{GA}$, $\overrightarrow{GB}$, and $\overrightarrow{GC}$ have zero resultant. So if, for example, we complete the parallelogram $CGBK$, we see that GK is an extension of AG and of the same length as AG. Thus, by merely rearranging the original relation between position vectors in terms of differences of these vectors (a rearrangement that is only possible if the original relation is independent of the origin), we come out with a geometrical theorem.]

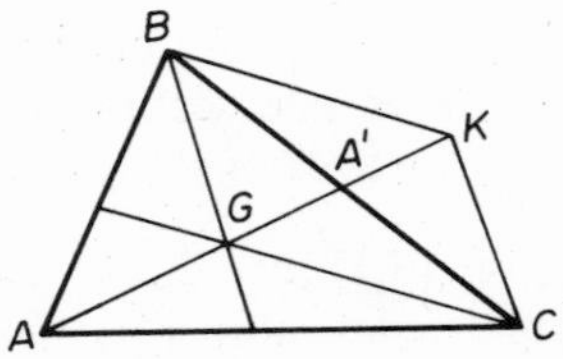

Exercise 3.20 In Exercise 3.19, one could rewrite the relation in the form $3(\mathbf{g}-\mathbf{a})+2(\mathbf{a}-\mathbf{b})+(\mathbf{b}-\mathbf{c})=0$. Interpret this geometrically. [It is easier to see what is involved if one rewrites this as $\frac{3}{2}(\mathbf{g}-\mathbf{a})+(\mathbf{a}-\mathbf{b})+\frac{1}{2}(\mathbf{b}-\mathbf{c})=0$.]

Exercise 3.21 A, B, C, and D are four points not necessarily in the same plane. Using position vectors, prove that if the line segments AC and BD bisect each other, $ABCD$ is a parallelogram. [*Hint:* rearrange $(\mathbf{a}+\mathbf{c})/2=(\mathbf{b}+\mathbf{d})/2$ to obtain $\mathbf{a}-\mathbf{b}=\mathbf{c}-\mathbf{d}$.]

Exercise 3.22 Extend Exercise 3.17 to the case of n position vectors $\mathbf{a}_1, \mathbf{a}_2, \ldots, \mathbf{a}_n$.

Let A be a fixed point and $\mathbf{c}$ a given vector. How can we represent the line through A parallel to $\mathbf{c}$? If P is any point on this line, and the position vectors of A and P are $\mathbf{a}$ and $\mathbf{r}$, respectively, then, since AP is parallel to $\mathbf{c}$,

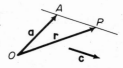

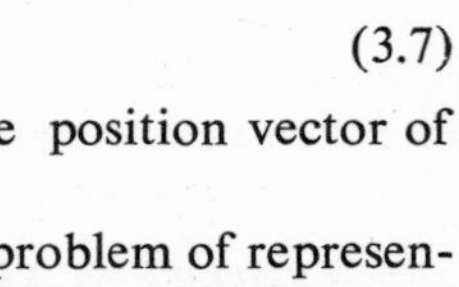

$$\mathbf{r}-\mathbf{a}=\mathbf{c}t, \tag{3.6}$$

where t is a parameter. We may rewrite this as

$$\mathbf{r}=\mathbf{a}+\mathbf{c}t, \tag{3.7}$$

and this represents the line in the sense that it gives the position vector of every point on the line in terms of the parameter t.

Consider now the analogous problem of representing the straight line through two points A and B with position vectors $\mathbf{a}$ and $\mathbf{b}$. Here we have merely to replace $\mathbf{c}$ in Equation (3.6) or (3.7) by $\mathbf{b}-\mathbf{a}$, since the line is certainly parallel to the vector $\mathbf{b}-\mathbf{a}$ inasmuch as it actually lies along AB. So we have

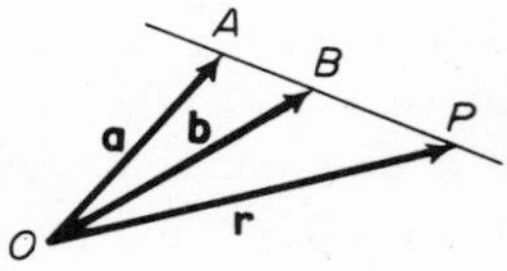

$$\mathbf{r}-\mathbf{a}=(\mathbf{b}-\mathbf{a})t \tag{3.8}$$

or

$$\mathbf{r} = \mathbf{a} + (\mathbf{b} - \mathbf{a})t. \tag{3.9}$$

Now a seeming puzzle arises. If we write Equation (3.7) in the form:

$$\mathbf{r} - \mathbf{a} - t\mathbf{c} = 0$$

and Equation (3.9) in the form:

$$\mathbf{r} + (t - 1)\mathbf{a} - t\mathbf{b} = 0,$$

we see that the sum of the coefficients in the latter is $1 + (t - 1) - t$, which is zero, whereas the corresponding sum in the former is $1 - 1 - t$, which is not zero. It appears, then, that Equation (3.9) is independent of the origin but (3.7) is not. This is not true, though, or rather, it is true that this *appears* to be the case, but it is actually not the case. Both equations are independent of the origin. This is clear from the fact that (3.6) involves only $(\mathbf{r} - \mathbf{a})$ and $\mathbf{c}$, each of which is independent of the origin. Where is the fallacy? [*Hint:* Why is $\mathbf{c}$ independent of the origin? Is it a position vector? What is the nature of the vectors $\mathbf{a}_1, \ldots, \mathbf{a}_n$ in Equation (3.5)? Does Equation (3.7) fall within the category of (3.5), or is it more general?]

All this preoccupation with vectorial relations that are independent of the origin can be misleading. It is a standard preoccupation, and it is forced on us because we are using those hybrid things, position vectors. But it obscures a crucial point. With what we may refer to as nonposition vectors, i. e., vectors of the usual type, relations such as

$$\overrightarrow{AM} = \overrightarrow{MB} \quad \text{and} \quad \mathbf{U} + 2\mathbf{V} = 5\mathbf{W}$$

are automatically independent of any choice of origin. They are, in fact, objective. And the objectivity of such vectorial relations is one of the most valuable attributes of vectors. Bear it in mind. It will play a crucial role later.

4. COORDINATES

Let $\mathbf{r}$ be the position vector of a point P relative to a reference frame defined by vectors $\mathbf{e}_x$, $\mathbf{e}_y$, and $\mathbf{e}_z$ starting at an origin O. The components of $\mathbf{r}$ relative to this frame are called the *coordinates* of P relative to the frame, and they are usually denoted by (x, y, z). [We are here considering the three-dimensional case, of course.] Thus,

$$\mathbf{r} = x\mathbf{e}_x + y\mathbf{e}_y + z\mathbf{e}_z. \tag{4.1}$$

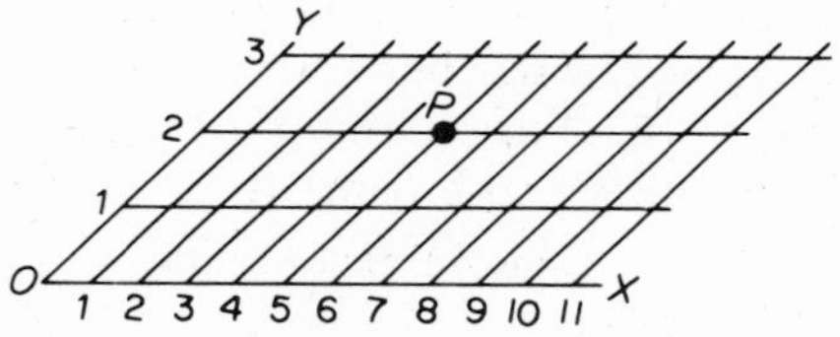

Figure 4.1

Note that while all vectors have components, only the components of *position* vectors are called coordinates. The coordinates here defined are of a restricted sort called *Cartesian coordinates.* Polar coordinates, and other curvilinear or nonuniform types of coordinates are not of this sort.

If we use Cartesian coordinates in two dimensions we are, in effect, using *graph paper* of the type shown in Figure 4.1, the point P having the coordinates (5, 2). Note that the scales along the two axes, though uniform, are not necessarily the same.

Exercise 4.1 In Figure 4.1, which vector has the greater magnitude, $\mathbf{e}_x$ or $\mathbf{e}_y$?

It is not so easy to draw a corresponding diagram of a three-dimensional Cartesian coordinate mesh: the diagram tends to become confusing.

Exercise 4.2 Draw such a diagram and see for yourself.

Exercise 4.3 Two points A and B have coordinates (x_1, y_1, z_1), (x_2, y_2, z_2) relative to a given reference frame. Prove that the coordinates of the mid-point, M, of AB are: $\left(\frac{x_1 + x_2}{2}, \frac{y_1 + y_2}{2}, \frac{z_1 + z_2}{2}\right)$. [*Hint*: Merely consider the coordinates of the position vectors in the vectorial form of the mid-point formula in Equation (3.1).]

Exercise 4.4 In Exercise 4.3, if P is a point on AB such that $AP/PB = m_1/m_2$, show that the coordinates of P are: $\left(\frac{m_2 x_1 + m_1 x_2}{m_1 + m_2}, \frac{m_2 y_1 + m_1 y_2}{m_1 + m_2}, \frac{m_2 z_1 + m_1 z_2}{m_1 + m_2}\right)$.

Exercise 4.5 Work out Exercises 3.5 and 3.7 using coordinates throughout. Note that, in effect, one does the same thing three times, once for the x-coordinates, once for the y, and once for the z.

Exercise 4.6 Prove, first in terms of vectors and then in terms of coordinates, that the lines joining the vertices of any tetrahedron to the points of intersection of the medians of the opposite faces intersect at a point that divides each of the lines in the ratio 3: 1.

Exercise 4.7 Show that, as t changes, the point with coordinates $(a_x + tc_x, a_y + tc_y, a_z + tc_z)$ moves along a straight line, the a's and c's being constants. [Use Equation (3.7).]

When the reference frame is defined by a unit orthogonal triad of vectors, the corresponding coordinates are called *rectangular Cartesian coodinates.* [I suppose that, strictly speaking, this term should apply also to the case in which $\mathbf{e}_x$, $\mathbf{e}_y$, $\mathbf{e}_z$ are mutually perpendicular but do not have unit magnitudes or even equal magnitudes. But we shall use it only for the above coordinates.] In two dimensions, the corresponding graph paper is of the familiar sort.

Exercise 4.8 Show that, in rectangular Cartesian coordinates, the distance from the origin of a point with coordinates (x, y, z) is $\sqrt{x^2 + y^2 + z^2}$.

Exercise 4.9 Points A and B have rectangular Cartesian coordinates (x_1, y_1, z_1), (x_2, y_2, z_2). Show that the vector represented by $\overrightarrow{AB}$ has components $(x_2 - x_1, y_2 - y_1, z_2 - z_1)$ and thus that the distance AB is $\sqrt{(x_2 - x_1)^2 + (y_2 - y_1)^2 + (z_2 - z_1)^2}$.

5 DIRECTION COSINES

In Figure 5.1 the lines OX, OY, and OZ are mutually perpendicular and lie along the positive directions of the vectors (not shown) **i**, **j**, and **k** of a unit orthogonal triad. These three lines are called *coordinate axes.* [They extend indefinitely on both sides of O, of course. The diagram shows only a

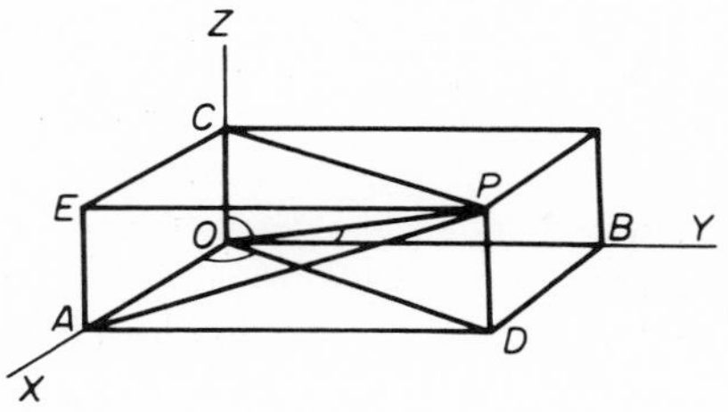

Figure 5.1

portion of each coordinate axis.] The line segment OP is a diagonal of the rectangular parallelepiped shown. There are many right angles in the diagram that are not readily recognized as such.

Exercise 5.1 Which pairs of lines meeting at the point D are at right angles? [There are four such pairs.] Also, which pairs of lines meeting at the point A are at right angles? [There are four—and that is without counting AX and AO as distinct lines; otherwise the count would be seven.]

We wish to specify in a convenient way the direction of OP relative to **i**, **j**, and **k**. There are various possible ways. For example, we could state the angle through which the plane OPC has swung about OC from the plane AOC, and the angle in the plane OPC that the line OP makes with the line OC; that is, we could state the two angles AOD and COP. Alternatively, we could use other appropriate pairs of angles. In certain cases describing the direction in terms of two angles is both convenient and useful. Indeed, the two angles AOD and COP are those used in what are called spherical polar coordinates.

There is a different method of specifying the direction of OP. It has the advantage of being symmetrical. But it uses *three* angles, and these angles, when first encountered, seem about as awkward a trio as one could imagine.

They are the three angles AOP, BOP, and COP, that OP makes with the three axes OX, OY, and OZ. These angles, denoted respectively by α, β, and γ, do not lie in one plane. Moreover, since any two of them suffice to determine the direction of OP, the three can not be independent of one another and, therefore, there must be a relation between them.

Exercise 5.2 Is it strictly correct to say that any two of these angles suffice to determine the direction of OP? [For a given α, OP will be on a certain cone. For given β, it will be on another cone. Consider how these cones intersect.]

We may by now be wondering what merits the angles α, β, and γ can have that will outweigh the above disadvantages. But this is because we have, in a sense, told the story backwards. Mathematicians did not arbitrarily pick three queer angles to do the work of two seemingly more sensible ones. Let us look at the situation from a different point of view.

Consider OP as a vector $\mathbf{V}$ with components (V_x, V_y, V_z) relative to $\mathbf{i}$, $\mathbf{j}$, and $\mathbf{k}$. Then if we know the components, we know the vector, and therefore, in particular, its direction. But if h is any number (greater than zero) the vector $h\mathbf{V}$ has the same direction as $\mathbf{V}$. Let us specify the direction, then, by means of the components of a vector of unit magnitude lying along $\mathbf{V}$. This unit vector is $(1/V)\,\mathbf{V}$, where V is the magnitude of $\mathbf{V}$:

$$V = \sqrt{V_x^2 + V_y^2 + V_z^2}. \tag{5.1}$$

The components of the unit vector, denoted by l, m, and n, are given by

$$l = \frac{V_x}{V}, \qquad m = \frac{V_y}{V}, \qquad n = \frac{V_z}{V}; \tag{5.2}$$

and we easily see that

$$l^2 + m^2 + n^2 = 1, \tag{5.3}$$

so that any two of the quantities l, m, and n automatically determine the third, to within a sign.

Having thus come upon these quantities l, m, and n, we now ask what they look like on a diagram. Let us look at triangle POA in Figure 5.1. Since OA is perpendicular to the plane PDA, it is perpendicular to every line in that plane, and therefore to the line AP. So despite appearances to the contrary, angle OAP is a right angle. In the right triangle OAP, the length of OA is V_x and the length of the hypotenuse OP is V. Therefore V_x/V, which is just l, is the cosine of the angle AOP that we have called α.

The coordinate planes OYZ, OZX, and OXY (called respectively the *yz*-plane, the *zx*-plane, and the *xy*-plane) separate the whole three-dimensional space into eight regions called *octants.* We have here discussed only the case in which OP points into what is called the first octant. When OP points into other octants, some or all of the angles AOP, BOP, and COP are obtuse and the corresponding cosines are negative.

Exercise 5.3 Prove that angle OBP is a right angle, and that m, which is V_y/V, equals $\cos \beta$. Prove also that $n = \cos \gamma$.

We see, then, that

$$l = \cos \alpha, \qquad m = \cos \beta, \qquad n = \cos \gamma; \tag{5.4}$$

and from Equation (5.3) we see that

$$\cos^2 \alpha + \cos^2 \beta + \cos^2 \gamma = 1. \tag{5.5}$$

The angles α, β, and γ that the line OP makes with the coordinate axes are called the *direction angles* of OP with respect to the reference frame; and the cosines of these angles are called its *direction cosines*. In practice, one works much more with the direction cosines than directly with the direction angles.

Though the line segments OP and PO are the same, the directions OP and PO are opposite, and if the direction cosines of the direction OP are l, m, and n, those of the direction PO are $-l$, $-m$, and $-n$. When we wish to stress that we are thinking of a given line (or line segment) as pointing in one rather than the other of the two directions associated with it, we call it a *directed* line (or line segment). Thus the x-axis, in its role as a coordinate axis, is a directed line rather than just a line, though we often think of it as just a line —as when we say that a point is 5 units away from it.

If a directed line or line segment does not pass through O, its direction can still be given in terms of direction cosines, since the direction is the same as that of a parallel directed line that does pass through O. Let points A and B have position vectors $\mathbf{r}_a$ and $\mathbf{r}_b$ relative to $\mathbf{i}$, $\mathbf{j}$, and $\mathbf{k}$, and let the coordinates of these points be (x_a, y_a, z_a), (x_b, y_b, z_b). Then the displacement $\overrightarrow{AB}$ has components $(x_b - x_a, y_b - y_a, z_b - z_a)$, and therefore its direction cosines are

$$\frac{x_b - x_a}{d}, \qquad \frac{y_b - y_a}{d}, \qquad \frac{z_b - z_a}{d} \tag{5.6}$$

where

$$d = \sqrt{(x_b - x_a)^2 + (y_b - y_a)^2 + (z_b - z_a)^2}. \tag{5.7}$$

Exercise 5.4 What are the direction cosines of $\mathbf{i}$? Work this out (a) by means of a diagram, and (b) purely algebraically, by means of Equation (5.2).

Exercise 5.5 If OP has direction cosines such that l and m are positive but n is negative, into which octant does it point? What if l and m were negative and n positive?

Exercise 5.6 A line lies in the plane of $\mathbf{i}$ and $\mathbf{j}$, and makes equal angles with the lines containing $\mathbf{i}$ and $\mathbf{j}$. What are its three direction cosines? Express them in terms of α only [There are four possible cases —two pairs of opposite directions. Had we spoken of *vectors* instead of *lines*, there would have been only two cases. Why?]

Exercise 5.7 A line makes equal angles with **i**, **j**, and **k**. What are its direction cosines if all are positive?

Exercise 5.8 A vector of magnitude V has direction cosines l, m, and n. What are its components? [*Ans.* (lV, mV, nV).]

Exercise 5.9 If two of the direction cosines of a vector are $\cos\theta \cos\varphi$ and $\cos\theta \sin\varphi$, what is the third direction cosine? [*Ans.* $\pm \sin\theta$.]

Exercise 5.10 If the direction cosines of a line are positive and in the ratio $2:3:4$, what are their actual values? [By Equation (5.3), the sum of the squares of the three direction cosines must be unity. But $2^2 + 3^2 + 4^2 = 29$. So we divide 2, 3, and 4 by $\sqrt{29}$ to obtain the direction cosines $2/\sqrt{29}$, $3/\sqrt{29}$, and $4/\sqrt{29}$. Three numbers that are *proportional* to direction cosines l, m, and n are called *direction numbers*.]

Exercise 5.11 A vector has direction numbers 1, 2, and 4. What are its direction cosines? [Two possibilities.]

6. ORTHOGONAL PROJECTIONS

We can get an idea of the usefulness and convenience of direction cosines by deriving some fundamental formulas of analytical geometry. We shall later derive these formulas by more compact vectorial methods, but the latter tend to obscure what is going on behind the scenes.

In deriving these formulas by means of direction cosines, we must make use of the idea of an *orthogonal projection*. Given a point P and a plane π, drop a perpendicular from P to π to meet π at the point P'. Then P' is called the orthogonal projection of P on the plane π. Given point P and a line λ, the foot, P', of the perpendicular from P to λ is called the orthogonal projection of P on the line λ.

Figure 6.1

There are other types of projection, but it will be safe in this book for us to drop the word "orthogonal" when speaking of orthogonal projections. The idea of such projections seems so simple that one wonders how it could possibly be worth considering. Yet it is actually a powerful mathematical concept, as we shall see.

If P traces out a curve, its projection, P, on a plane π traces out a curve called the projection on π of the original curve. If the curve is a plane curve and closed, the area enclosed by its projection on π is called the projection on π of the area enclosed by the original curve.

Exercise 6.1 What is the shape of the projection on π of a straight line? What of a triangle? What of a circle? [*Ans.* A straight line or a point; a triangle or a line segment; a circle, or an ellipse, or a line segment.]

Exercise 6.2 A rectangle $ABCD$ has AB lying in the plane π and BC making an angle θ with the plane. If K is the area of $ABCD$, show that the area of its projection on π is $K \cos \theta$.

No matter how a point P may move, its projection, P', on a line λ cannot move off the line. Two simple theorems form the basis of the applications of projections on a line.

Theorem 1. If a directed line segment AB of length d makes an angle θ with a directed line λ, the length and sign of its projection on λ are given by $d \cos \theta$; the sign is positive if the projection points in the same direction as λ and negative if it points in the opposite direction.

To prove this, pass planes through A and B that are perpendicular to λ and let them cut λ at A' and B'. Then A' and B' are the projections of A and B whether the line AB is coplanar with λ or not. If the segment AB is moved parallel to itself, with A and B remaining on the respective planes, the projections of A and B will be unaltered. So move AB to the position $A'B_1$, A' being the above-mentioned projection of A. Then from the right triangle $A'B'B_1$ we see that since $\cos \theta$ is negative when θ is obtuse, the length and sign of the projection, $A'B'$, are given by $d \cos \theta$.

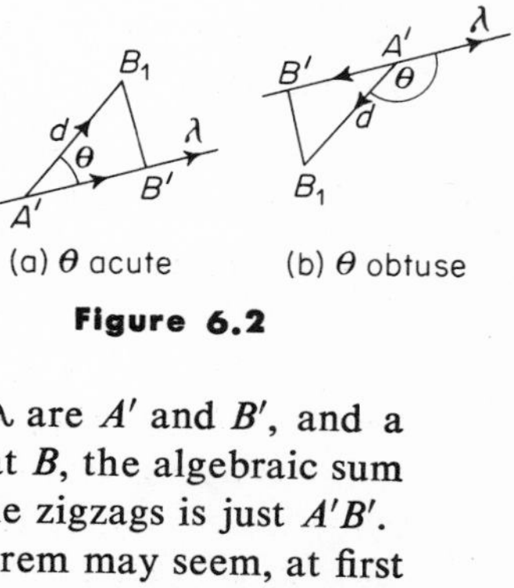

(a) θ acute (b) θ obtuse

Figure 6.2

Theorem 2. If the projections of A and B on line λ are A' and B', and a point P starting at A moves on a zigzag line ending at B, the algebraic sum of the projections on λ of the line segments forming the zigzags is just $A'B'$.

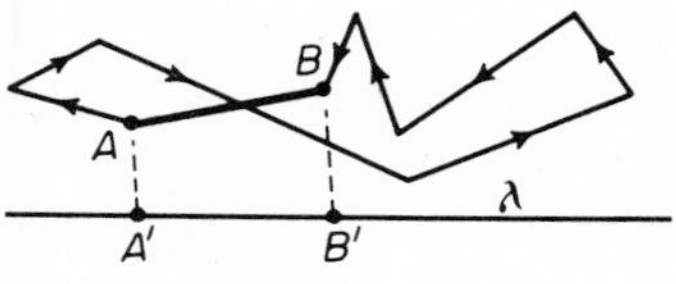

Figure 6.3

This powerful theorem may seem, at first glance, difficult to prove, especially when one realizes that the zigzag line need not lie in a plane but could even jut into four dimensions, or more. Yet the proof is almost a triviality, a fact that by no means lessens the theorem's importance. As P traces out its zigzag path from A to B, its projection, P', moves to and fro on the line λ starting at A' and ending at B'; and when, for example, P' retraces to the right ground previously traced out to the left, it cancels it. The *algebraic* sum of the projections is therefore $A'B'$. And that is that.

Exercise 6.3 Let O be the origin and A the point $(x, 0, 0)$. Let ON be a directed line segment having direction cosines l, m, and n. Show that the length and sign of the projection on ON of the directed line segment OA are given by lx whatever the signs of l and x. Also, if K is the point $(x, y, 0)$, show that the length and sign of the projection on ON of the directed line segment AK are similarly given by my. [Use Theorem 1. Note how conveniently direction cosines enter.]

To apply these two theorems, we first consider a plane such that ON, the perpendicular to it from the origin, has length p and direction cosines $l, m,$ and n. Let any point P on the plane have rectangular Cartesian coordinates (x, y, z). We wish to find the equation that x, y, and z must satisfy—an equation of the plane, as it is called. Drop a perpendicular from P to the xy-plane meeting it at K. Draw KA parallel to the y-axis to meet the x-axis at A. Then $OA = x$, $AK = y$, and $KP = z$. If and only if P lies in the plane, PN will be perpendicular to ON. Therefore:

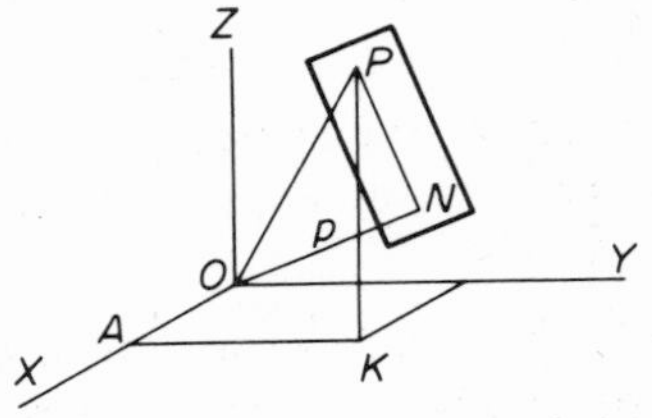

Figure 6.4

$$\text{projection of } OP \text{ on } ON = ON.$$

Using Theorem 2, we replace OP by the zigzag $OAKP$. Then:

$$\text{sum of projections of } OA,\ AK, \text{ and } KP \text{ on } ON = ON. \tag{6.1}$$

Applying Exercise 6.3, and remembering that the length of ON is p, we have immediately

$$lx + my + nz = p, \tag{6.2}$$

which is the equation we sought.

Exercise 6.4 How far from the origin is the plane whose equation is $3x + 2y - 6z = 63$?

Solution The first step is to resist the temptation to say, by comparison with Equation (6.2), that $l = 3$, $m = 2$, $n = 6$ and $p = 63$. Obviously something is wrong with such a method, since we could have rewritten the given equation as, say, $300x + 200y - 600z = 6300$, and thus have come to the conclusion that l is not 3 but 300, and similarly for m, n, and p. We have to remember that $l^2 + m^2 + n^2 = 1$. The numbers 3, 2, and -6 are not direction cosines but direction numbers (see Exercise 5.10). Since $\sqrt{3^2 + 2^2 + 6^2} = \sqrt{49} = 7$, we divide the given equation by 7 to obtain $\frac{3}{7}x + \frac{2}{7}y - \frac{6}{7}z = 9$. We may now make the identifications $l = \frac{3}{7}$, $m = \frac{2}{7}$, $n = \frac{6}{7}$, and therefore, also, $p = 9$.

Exercise 6.5 Like Exercise 6.4 for the planes $x - 2y + 2z = 108$, $x + y + z = 9$, and $3y + 4z = 100$.

Consider next the problem of finding a formula for the angle between two directed lines having direction cosines l, m, n and l', m', n' respectively.

[If two lines do not intersect, the angle between them is defined as the angle between lines parallel to them that do intersect. Actually there are infinitely many angles, both positive and negative, between two given lines. When we talk of "*the* angle" between them, we presumably have some specific one in mind. Here, as on previous occasions, we mean the smallest positive angle between the positive directions of the lines regarded as directed lines.]

Denote the angle between the two lines by θ, and for convenience (though it is not really necessary), imagine the lines emanating from the origin. Take points P and P' on the lines such that OP and OP' are of *unit* length. Then, by Theorem 1, the length and sign of the projection of OP on OP' will be given by just $\cos\theta$. But we can also compute the length and sign of the projection by using the zigzag path $OAKP$ instead of OP. Since OP is of unit length, the coordinates of p are just (l, m, n), so that $OA = l$, $AK = m$, and $KP = n$. These line segments, being parallel to the coordinate axes, make with OP' angles whose cosines are respectively l', m', and n'. Therefore the algebraic sum of the lengths of their projections on OP' is $ll' + mm' + nn'$. So we must have:

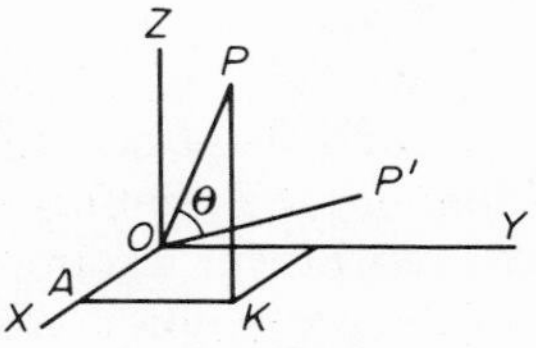

Figure 6.5

$$\cos\theta = ll' + mm' + nn'. \tag{6.3}$$

Exercise 6.6 In the above, did we use the fact that OP' was of unit length? Derive Equation (6.3) by projecting OP' onto OP.

Exercise 6.7 Derive Equation (6.3) by projecting OP onto OP', but taking OP to be of arbitrary length C.

Exercise 6.8 Find the cosine of the angle between two lines with direction numbers 1, 3, 5 and 2, − 4, 3. $\left[\textit{Ans.}\ \frac{5}{\sqrt{35}\sqrt{29}}.\right]$

Exercise 6.9 Prove that two lines are perpendicular if their direction cosines satisfy

$$ll' + mm' + nn' = 0. \tag{6.4}$$

Exercise 6.10 Find the cosine of the angle between the planes $x + 3y + 5z = 10$ and $2x - 4y + 3z = 15$. [The angle is the same as that between the normals to the planes, and these normals have direction numbers 1, 3, 5 and 2, − 4, 3 respectively.]

Exercise 6.11 The xy-plane has an equation $z = 0$, and the yz-plane $x = 0$. Using Equation (6.4), verify that these planes are perpendicular.

Exercise 6.12 What is the distance between the two parallel planes $x + 2y + z = 2$ and $x + 2y + z = 8$?

7. PROJECTIONS OF AREAS

In Exercise 6.2 we found that if rectangle $ABCD$ makes an angle θ with a plane π through AB, the area of its projection is $\cos\theta$ times the area of $ABCD$. This is strongly reminiscent of the way projections of line segments behave, as given in Theorem 1. And the result is not confined to rectangles having one side in the plane of projection. It is not even confined to rectangles.

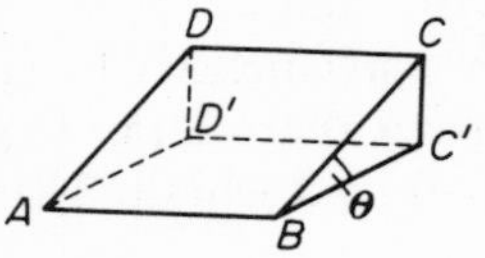

Figure 7.1

If we have a plane area of quite irregular shape, as in Figure 7.2, we can crisscross it with lines to break it up into a lot of rectangles—with some left-overs of irregular shape next to the boundary. Ignore the left-overs for the moment and consider the resulting serrated-edged region. Since the area of the projection of its constituent rectangles is $\cos\theta$ times the area of the original, the total area of the projection is $\cos\theta$ times that of the original serrated-edged region. So, for this region, the area of the projection is $\cos\theta$ times that of the original. The finer the crisscross mesh, the more nearly the serrated-edged region fills the over-all region, and it will hardly come as a surpise that, by methods belonging to the calculus, one can prove that the result actually holds for the over-all region too. Thus we have the important theorem that if a plane region of any shape has an area K, the area of its projection on a plane making an angle θ with it is $K\cos\theta$. We shall use this result in a later chapter.

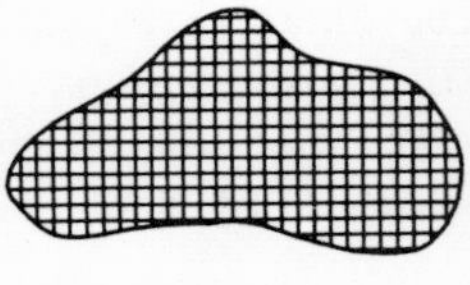

Figure 7.2

Exercise 7.1 In Figure 7.1, take two points M and L on the line DC such that $ML = DC$. Show that the area of the parallelogram $ABLM$ is equal to that of the rectangle $ABCD$. Hence, show that the area of the projection of this parallelogram is $\cos\theta$ times the area of the parallelogram.

Exercise 7.2 A circular disc of radius 5 inches touches the ground, which is horizontal, and lies in a plane that is inclined at 45° to the ground. If the sun is vertically overhead, what is the area of the shadow of the disc, what is the time of day, and where on earth can the disc be?

4

SCALARS. SCALAR PRODUCTS

1. UNITS AND SCALARS

The components of a vector $\mathbf{V}$ depend on the frame of reference. They change when we go from one frame to another. For example, if a displacement $\mathbf{V}$ lies in the plane of $\mathbf{e}_x$ and $\mathbf{e}_y$ as indicated on the left of Figure 1.1, its components $(\mathbf{V}_x, \mathbf{V}_y, \mathbf{V}_z)$ are such that $\mathbf{V}_x, \mathbf{V}_y \neq 0$, $\mathbf{V}_z = 0$. If we go over to a new reference frame in which $\mathbf{e}'_x$ and $\mathbf{e}'_z$ are the same as $\mathbf{e}_x$ and $\mathbf{e}_z$ but $\mathbf{e}'_y$ lies along $\mathbf{V}$, as on the right of Figure 1.1, then the new components $(\mathbf{V}'_x, \mathbf{V}'_y, \mathbf{V}'_z)$ are such that $\mathbf{V}'_x = 0$, $\mathbf{V}'_y \neq 0$, and $\mathbf{V}'_z = 0$. Even when we merely change the magnitudes of the base vectors $\mathbf{e}_x$, $\mathbf{e}_y$, and $\mathbf{e}_z$ without altering their directions, the components of $\mathbf{V}$ are altered—unless $\mathbf{V}$ is the zero vector, of course. Nevertheless, no matter how we change the reference system, the vector itself remains the same [remember, here, the discussion we had earlier of the master reference frame], and in particular the magnitude of $\mathbf{V}$ remains the same.

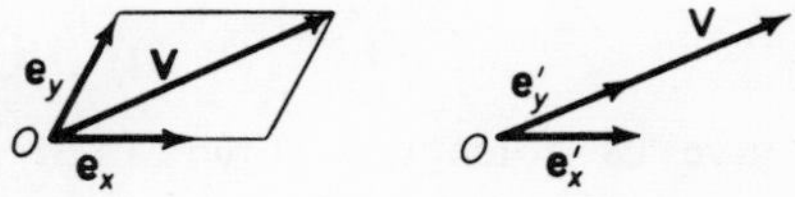

Figure 1.1

Exercise 1.1 A displacement $\mathbf{V}$ points along the $\mathbf{e}_x$ direction and has magnitude V. Its components are therefore $(V/e_x, 0, 0)$, where e_x is the magnitude of $\mathbf{e}_x$. What will its components be if we go over to a new reference frame in which $\mathbf{e}'_x$ has twice the magnitude of $\mathbf{e}_x$? [*Ans.* $(V/2e_x, 0, 0)$.]

We must now make a subtle distinction. Suppose that the displacement **V** has a magnitude of 108 inches, that the base vectors $\mathbf{e}_x$, $\mathbf{e}_y$, and $\mathbf{e}_z$ have each a magnitude of 1 inch, and that the components of **V** are (36, 24, 72). If we go over to a new reference frame in which the base vectors $\mathbf{e}'_x$, $\mathbf{e}'_y$, and $\mathbf{e}'_z$ differ from $\mathbf{e}_x$, $\mathbf{e}_y$, and $\mathbf{e}_z$ only in that their magnitudes are 12 inches instead of 1 inch, the components of **V** change to one-twelfth of their former values, i. e., to (3, 2, 6). Nevertheless the magnitude of **V** is still 108 inches. Its numerical value, 108, has not changed. Suppose, though, that we go back to the original reference frame and *without altering the base vectors or the vector* **V**, we use a different scale of measurement for all lengths, going from inches to feet. Then the components of **V** will still be (36, 24, 72) since they are the *ratios* of the magnitudes of the component vectors of **V** to the magnitudes of the e's and thus are independent of the scale of measurement. But, though the magnitude of **V** is the same as before, its *numerical* value has changed from 108 to 9, because we are now measuring the magnitude in feet instead of inches.

Exercise 1.2 What will the components of **V** be relative to the foregoing $\mathbf{e}'_x$, $\mathbf{e}'_y$, and $\mathbf{e}'_z$, when we go over from measuring in inches to measuring in feet? [*Ans.* (3, 2, 6), just as they were when we used inches in this reference frame.]

Exercise 1.3 A force **F** has a magnitude of 6 lbs., and is represented by an arrow-headed line segment of length 6 inches. Its components relative to $\mathbf{e}_x$, $\mathbf{e}_y$, and $\mathbf{e}_z$ are (4, 1, 3). If the reference frame is changed to one with new base vectors $\mathbf{e}'_x$, $\mathbf{e}'_y$, and $\mathbf{e}'_z$ where $\mathbf{e}'_x = 10\mathbf{e}_y$, $\mathbf{e}'_y = 20\mathbf{e}_z$, and $\mathbf{e}'_z = 30\mathbf{e}_x$, what will be the new components of **F**? [*Ans.* $(\frac{1}{10}, \frac{3}{20}, \frac{2}{15})$.]

If the components of the displacement **V** are pure numbers, how can Equation (2.5) of chapter 3, namely,

$$V = \sqrt{V_x^2 + V_y^2 + V_z^2},$$

give us a length? How can it give us anything but a pure number? It is a standard equation, found in one guise or another in practically all textbooks on vectors. Let us consider it more carefully.

The fact is that we glossed over the question of units in deriving it. The legerdemain occurs in Equation (2.3) of Chapter 3. To keep the wording simple, let us discuss here the case in which all quantities involved are positive. If OA means the length of the line segment OA, then it is not a pure number and so can not be equal to $\mathbf{V}_x$. It is really equal to $\mathbf{V}_x i$, where i is the magnitude of **i** and thus a length. Since i has the numerical value 1, it can be omitted—provided we realize that it is really there. Equation (2.5) of Chapter 3 can thus be regarded as yielding a length after all, though this would have been clearer had we written it as

$$V = \sqrt{V_x^2 i^2 + V_y^2 j^2 + V_z^2 k^2},$$

which corresponds (except for the taking of the square root) to Equation (2.1) of Chapter 3 for the case of a unit orthogonal triad. It was this sort of thing, among others, that we had in mind when we said there that the price of using such triads is loss of generality and loss of depth of understanding.

For a displacement **V**, which has a magnitude that is a length, the problem of units is relatively straightforward. What of a different sort of vector, such as a force **F**? The remark in Exercise 1.3 that the 6 lbs. is represented by 6 inches is less innocent than it seems. Forces combine by the parallelogram law with forces, not with displacements, whether the latter are thought of as localized or not. Therefore, a force cannot be equivalent to the vectorial sum of three such displacements. Strictly speaking, instead of writing an equation like

$$\mathbf{F} = F_x \mathbf{e}_x + F_y \mathbf{e}_y + F_z \mathbf{e}_z, \tag{1.1}$$

and thinking of the **e**'s as *geometrical* vectors having magnitudes that are lengths, we should write something like

$$\mathbf{F} = F_x \mathbf{f}_x + F_y \mathbf{f}_y + F_z \mathbf{f}_z, \tag{1.2}$$

where **F** and the **f**'s are all forces, and the components F_x, F_y, and F_z are pure numbers. If we did this consistently with all types of vectors, the components would always be dimensionless numbers. But when working with vectors we like to draw arrow-headed line segments and parallelograms, and it is difficult to resist the temptation to think of the arrow-headed line segments as lengths. [We can hardly formulate the parallelogram law without thinking geometrically in this way. Compare page 9, where we explained the sense in which forces are vectors.] So we usually express **F** as in Equation (1.1) of this chapter. But, to clarify matters, let us here make a distinction between **F**, the force, and its geometrical counterpart, which we shall denote by $\mathscr{F}$. This $\mathscr{F}$ has a magnitude that is a length; for example, each pound of force could correspond to an inch of $\mathscr{F}$. Then if we write

$$\mathscr{F} = \mathscr{F}_x \mathbf{e}_x + \mathscr{F}_y \mathbf{e}_y + \mathscr{F}_z \mathbf{e}_z, \tag{1.3}$$

the components $\mathscr{F}_x$, $\mathscr{F}_y$, and $\mathscr{F}_z$ are pure numbers and are, in fact, the same as the F_x, F_y, and F_z in Equation (1.2)—but not the same as those in Equation (1.1). For we can go from Equation (1.2) to Equation (1.1) by changing *all* lbs. into inches. But when we write Equation (1.1), we are apt to think of **F** as in lbs., not inches. In this case we have to say that the components F_x, F_y, and F_z in Equation (1.1) are not pure numbers, but have the dimensions of a force divided by a length. When we then calculate the magnitude of **F** in terms of its components, we have to remember to bring in the magnitudes of the base vectors, the quantities $\mathscr{F}_x \mathbf{e}_x$, etc. being thus forces. Similar considerations apply to other vector quantities such as velocities, accelerations, and others we shall come upon later.

Exercise 1.4 Force **F** has a magnitude of 6 lbs. and is represented by an arrow-headed line segment of length 6 inches. Its components F_x, F_y, and F_z relative to $\mathbf{e}_x$, $\mathbf{e}_y$, and $\mathbf{e}_z$ are (4, 1, 3). (a) What are its components relative to corresponding vectors $\mathbf{f}_x$, $\mathbf{f}_y$, and $\mathbf{f}_z$ with magnitudes that are in lbs? (b) What are the components, $\mathscr{F}_x$, $\mathscr{F}_y$, and $\mathscr{F}_z$ of $\mathscr{F}$ relative to $\mathbf{e}_x$, $\mathbf{e}_y$, and $\mathbf{e}_z$? [*Ans.* (4, 1, 3) in each case.]

Exercise 1.5 In Exercise 1.4, let the unit of force be changed from the lb. to the oz. (but with each lb. represented by 1 inch as before). What are the answers to (a) and (b) in this case? [*Ans.* The same as before. Which components *do* change?]

Exercise 1.6 In Exercise 1.4, if we changed from one inch per lb. to one inch per oz., what would happen to the three sets of components mentioned therein? [*Ans.* Those in (a) and (b) would be unaltered. Those of **F** relative to $\mathbf{e}_x$, $\mathbf{e}_y$, and $\mathbf{e}_z$ would become (64, 16, 48).]

If a force has a magnitude of 6 lbs. and we change the unit of force from lbs. to oz., the *numerical* value of its magnitude changes to 96.

A magnitude that is objective in the sense that it does not change simply because we change the reference frame, though it *may* change its numerical measure when we change the scale of measurement, is called a *scalar*. Thus the magnitude of a vector is a scalar. But a scalar need not be associated with a vector. For example, the number of fingers on one's hand is a scalar. So are the mass of a body and the time interval between two events, according to Newtonian physics. A scalar need not be constant. For example, the height of a growing child is a scalar.

Exercise 1.7 Name various other scalars. [Do not be content with "the number of fingers on two hands," "the number of fingers on three hands if one finger has been chopped off," and the like. Give various types of scalars including variable ones.]

Exercise 1.8 Could the number of fingers on one's hand change because of a change of units? [This would make an excellent true-false question, because the answer is both yes and no. It depends on what we mean by *number*. If we mean that we can put the fingers in one-to-one correspondence with five pebbles, say, then the number will not change. But we can change the unit of counting: for example, we can count in dozens, in which case the *number* of fingers becomes 5/12. Thus, even a dimensionless number can be changed by a change of unit.]

Exercise 1.9 Is the angle between two vectors having the same starting point a scalar? Is the area of the parallelogram defined by the two vectors a scalar?

Not everything that has magnitude is a scalar. For instance, the components of a vector are not scalars since they change when the reference system is changed. [But the "components" *relative to a particular* $\mathbf{e}_x$, $\mathbf{e}_y$, $\mathbf{e}_z$ are scalars since these "components" are really related not to a reference frame regarded as such but to a particular set of fixed vectors $\mathbf{e}_x$, $\mathbf{e}_y$, $\mathbf{e}_z$.] The number of vertices of a given triangle, namely 3, is a scalar, but the number of vertices lying in coordinate planes is not.

Exercise 1.10 Why not?

Note how long it has taken us to get to a place where we could try to define a scalar satisfactorily. Even so we have cheated. In Chapter 1 we pointed out the difficulty of giving satisfactory definitions that are brief. Have you noticed that though we have used the word *magnitude* freely, we have never defined it? We have no intention of doing so. But you might like to try for yourself.

Exercise 1.11 Define *magnitude*. [You may come up with a definition along these lines: *magnitude is someting that can be represented by a single number*. This is not satisfactory, though, for two opposite reasons. One is that we may need different numbers for the same magnitude in different units, so that the word "single" might need qualification despite the word "can." The other is that, by means of a code, we can represent pretty well anything by a single number. Anyway, what about such a thing as your telephone number? Perhaps we have to insist that numbers representing magnitudes of the same sort shall combine according to the usual arithmetical laws of addition. This sounds promising. It would exclude catalog numbers, telephone numbers, and other code numbers. But suppose we chose to measure weights by the *logarithms* of the numbers of pounds in them. Then, since for example $\log 2 + \log 5 = \log 2 \times 5 = \log 10$ which is not $\log 7$, would this fact mean that we could not regard the weight of a piece of matter as a magnitude? One would prefer that it did not. Evidently some rewording is necessary. Keep at it —if you are so inclined. And when you have overcome this particular difficulty, ask yourself whether temperature is a magnitude.]

Exercise 1.12 Is the magnitude of a position vector a scalar? [This is not a question to be answered with a simple yes or no. It has facets. Think it through.]

Given a vector $\mathbf{V}$ of magnitude V, we can form a new vector by multiplying the magnitude by a scalar, say h, and keeping the same direction and location. This new vector is denoted by $h\mathbf{V}$, and we say that it is the result of multiplying the vector $\mathbf{V}$ by the scalar h. We have already discussed this for the case in which h is a dimensionless number, and we have seen instances in which h was not. In the latter case, $h\mathbf{V}$ cannot combine with $\mathbf{V}$ according to the parallelogram law since it is not of the same sort as $\mathbf{V}$. For example, if $\mathbf{a}$ is the acceleration vector of a particle of mass m, then $m\mathbf{a}$ is not an acceleration vector; by Newton's second law of motion, we find that it actually combines with forces (see Equation (6.1) of Chapter 2).

2. SCALAR PRODUCTS

We have seen how the arithmetical symbols + and − can be used to represent the combination of vectors according to the parallelogram law. Having seen in this way how we can talk of *adding* and *subtracting* vectors, we naturally ask ourselves how we can *multiply* and *divide* vectors. But actually there is no reason—except perhaps misguided optimism—why we should expect to be able to do so usefully. For example, though we can "add" colors (as on a color television screen) or "subtract" them (as in amateur color photography), it does not occur to us to ask how we could multiply or divide colors by colors. Again, we can add and subtract money; and if we are astute and lucky, we can multiply money—but by numbers, not by money. If we start with $ 100 and triple our money, we end up with $ 300 which is $ 100 multiplied by 3, not multiplied by $ 3. We *could* contemplate the idea of multiplying $ 100 by $ 3 and getting 300 "square dollars," but even apart from the name we would not feel that the idea was likely to be particularly useful. What right have we, then, to expect that there is even any meaning to "**U** times **V**" or "**U** divided by **V**"?

Let us see what we can think of that might be somehow worthy of the phrase "**U** times **V**." Given two vectors **U** and **V** with magnitudes U and V, we could form the scalar UV which would be a sort of product of the vectors **U** and **V**. But it is really just the product of the two scalars U and V, and it does not involve the directions of the vectors at all.

We can bring in the directions to some extent by considering the angle between **U** and **V**. Let us call it θ. The angle θ does not tell us everything about the directions of **U** and **V**. It tells us only one quarter of the total amount of information about the directions, since two angles are needed to specify each direction; thus, θ is one angle out of a needed four. It has the advantage, though, of being a scalar.

Using θ as well as the magnitudes U and V, we can form all kinds of scalars that involve the product of the magnitudes. For example, $UV\theta$, $UV\theta^5$, $UV\sin\theta$, $UV\cos\theta$, $UV\tan\theta$, $UV\sec\theta$, $UV\sin^3\theta\cos\theta$, $UV\sin\theta/\theta^2$, and so on. Out of all these possibilities, there is one that has, shall we say, a pleasing geometrical significance: the quantity $UV\sin\theta$ gives the area of the parallelogram defined by **U** and **V**, as is easily seen. We might think, therefore, that this particular scalar quantity formed by multiplying various scalars connected with the vectors **U** and **V** would so merit our attention as to be worthy of some such title as the "scalar product" of the vectors **U** and **V**, a title that graces the name of this chapter. Why do we shrink from so regarding it? One reason, and it is a good one, is that we happen to know (as perhaps you do too) that the term "scalar product" is used for a different combination of U, V, and θ. But that is hardly an enlightening reason. Let us see what makes us reluctant to give $UV\sin\theta$ the particular honor of the title "scalar product."

The trouble with $UV\sin\theta$ comes to light when we consider the parallelogram law. Suppose vectors **A**, **B**, and **C** are such that **C** is the resultant of **A** and **B**. We write this fact in the form

$$\mathbf{C} = \mathbf{A} + \mathbf{B}, \tag{2.1}$$

and we say that **C** is equivalent to **A** and **B** combined. Now if we really mean the word "equivalent," we will want the "scalar product" of a vector **V** with **C** to be the same as the scalar product of **V** with **A** + **B**. We can always ensure this by saying that **A** + **B** is just another way of saying **C**. But we would prefer to be able to say the more stringent, and more significant thing that the "scalar product" of **V** with the resultant (**A** + **B**) is the same as that of **V** with **A** plus that of **V** with **B**; that is, we would like the "scalar product" to obey the distributive law.

It is easy to see that $UV \sin \theta$ does not obey this law. Take, for simplicity, a vector **V** that is perpendicular to **A**, **B**, and **C**, as in Figure 2.1. Then, unless **A** and **B** have the same direction, the area of the rectangle formed by **V** and **C** is clearly smaller than the sum of the areas of the rectangle formed by **V** and **A** and the rectangle formed by **V** and **B**. This is because the magnitude of **C** is smaller than the sum of the magnitudes of **A** and **B**. Naturally, we are disappointed. The quantity $UV \sin \theta$ has such a pleasant geometrical significance that we are reluctant to see it fail our test. But it is not lost to us. We shall find a way to make it pass the test—at a price. That, however, comes later.

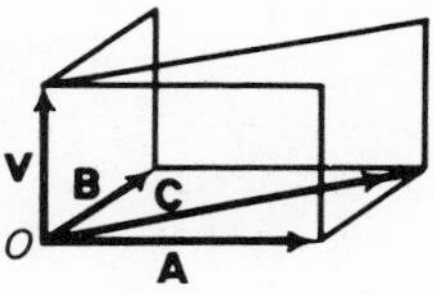

Figure 2.1

Meanwhile the foregoing gives us an important hint. Though the magnitudes of **A** and **B** do not add up to the magnitude of **C**, we recall Theorem 2 about projections, and we realize that it tells us, in effect, that the sum of the *projections* of **A** and **B**—on *any* line—is equal to the projection of **C** on that line. Let us see how we can profit from this fact. Take a vector **V** and project the vectors **A**, **B**, and **C** onto it. Then:

$$\text{projection of } \mathbf{C} = \text{projection of } \mathbf{A} + \text{projection of } \mathbf{B}.$$

If θ_{AV}, θ_{BV}, and θ_{CV} are the angles that **A**, **B**, and **C** make with **V**, this can be written, by Theorem 1, as

$$C \cos \theta_{CV} = A \cos \theta_{AV} + B \cos \theta_{BV}. \tag{2.2}$$

Therefore, if we define the scalar product of **V** with **U** as $U \cos \theta_{UV}$, and denote it by $\mathbf{V \cdot U}$, we see that Equation (2.2) yields:

$$\mathbf{V \cdot C} = \mathbf{V \cdot (A + B)} = \mathbf{V \cdot A} + \mathbf{V \cdot B}.$$

This is good as far as it goes, but such a quantity $\mathbf{V \cdot U}$ would not be the same as $\mathbf{U \cdot V}$: the former would be $U \cos \theta$, the latter $V \cos \theta$, where θ is the angle between **U** and **V**. There is no reason why we should insist that $\mathbf{V \cdot U} = \mathbf{U \cdot V}$, but it happens that there is a simple way of making this relation true, so we might as well make the most of our opportunity. We modify the above by regarding $\mathbf{U}\cdot\mathbf{V}$ not as $U \cos \theta$ but as $UV \cos \theta$. Let us make this official:

"Let **U** and **V** be two vectors with magnitudes U and V, the angle between the vectors being θ. The scalar $UV \cos \theta$ is denoted by the symbol $\mathbf{U}\cdot\mathbf{V}$ and is called the scalar product, or the dot product, of **U** and **V**."

Thus,

$$\mathbf{U}\cdot\mathbf{V} = UV \cos \theta. \tag{2.3}$$

In particular, we see that

$$\mathbf{V}\cdot\mathbf{V} = V^2. \tag{2.4}$$

Exercise 2.1 Is $(\mathbf{A}\cdot\mathbf{B})\cdot\mathbf{C} = \mathbf{A}\cdot(\mathbf{B}\cdot\mathbf{C})$? [*Ans.* In a nonsensical sense, *yes*, since neither has any meaning. Why not?]

Exercise 2.2 Prove that

$$\mathbf{U}\cdot\mathbf{V} = \mathbf{V}\cdot\mathbf{U}. \tag{2.5}$$

Exercise 2.3 Prove that if $\mathbf{C} = \mathbf{A} + \mathbf{B}$, then $\mathbf{V}\cdot\mathbf{C} = \mathbf{V}\cdot\mathbf{A} + \mathbf{V}\cdot\mathbf{B}$, i. e., that

$$\mathbf{V}\cdot(\mathbf{A} + \mathbf{B}) = \mathbf{V}\cdot\mathbf{A} + \mathbf{V}\cdot\mathbf{B}. \tag{2.6}$$

Exercise 2.4 What is the value of $\mathbf{U}\cdot\mathbf{V}$ if **U** and **V** are perpendicular? What if they have the same direction?

Exercise 2.5 Prove that if two opposite edges of a tetrahedron are perpendicular, and two other opposite edges are perpendicular, then the remaining two are also perpendicular. [Denote the vertices by P, Q, R, and S. Then we are given that $\overrightarrow{PQ}\cdot\overrightarrow{RS} = 0$, and $\overrightarrow{PR}\cdot\overrightarrow{QS} = 0$, say, and we wish to prove that $\overrightarrow{PS}\cdot\overrightarrow{QR} = 0$. We express everything in terms of vectors emanating from P. Thus $\overrightarrow{RS} = \overrightarrow{PS} - \overrightarrow{PR}$, etc. So, given $\overrightarrow{PQ}\cdot(\overrightarrow{PS} - \overrightarrow{PR}) = 0$ and $\overrightarrow{PR}\cdot(\overrightarrow{PS} - \overrightarrow{PQ}) = 0$, we wish to prove that $\overrightarrow{PS}\cdot(\overrightarrow{PR} - \overrightarrow{PQ}) = 0$, but this is an immediate consequence, as you can see by adding the two preceding relations.]

As happens often, though not always, that which is mathematically elegant turns out to be that which is important in applications. In the field of physics, consider the work done by a constant force **F** with magnitude F lbs. If it acts on a particle that moves through a distance D ft. in its own direction, it does an amount of work FD ft. lbs. Suppose that the displacement of the particle, **D**, is not along the line of action of the force. Then we can resolve the force **F** into two forces $\mathbf{F}_{//}$ and $\mathbf{F}_{\perp}$, the former lying along **D** and the latter perpendicular to it. The particle does not move in the direction of the

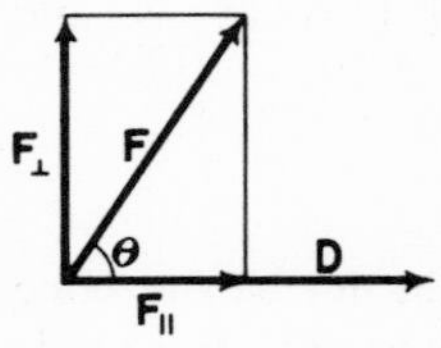

Figure 2.2

force $\mathbf{F}_\perp$ at all, and thus $\mathbf{F}_\perp$ does no work during the displacement. The force $\mathbf{F}_{//}$ lies along the displacement of the particle and since the magnitude of $\mathbf{F}_{//}$ is $F \cos \theta$, it does an amount of work $FD \cos \theta$ ft. lbs., which is thus the amount of work done by **F**. We see, then, that the work done is none other than the scalar product of **F** and **D**:

$$W = \mathbf{F} \cdot \mathbf{D}. \tag{2.7}$$

The above probably sounds like a convincing and enlightening argument. It may be enlightening, but it is not really convincing. It assumes, for example, that the work done by **F** can be found by adding the work done by $\mathbf{F}_\perp$ and the work done by $\mathbf{F}_{//}$, merely because $\mathbf{F} = \mathbf{F}_\perp + \mathbf{F}_{//}$; it also assumes that the work done by $\mathbf{F}_\perp$ is zero because the particle does not move in the direction of $\mathbf{F}_\perp$ at all.

Actually, the above argument is a valid *consequence* of the *definition* in Equation (2.7) of the work done by a constant force. It is not a derivation of that equation. From Equation (2.7) we can deduce the various assumptions made in the above argument. Without using calculus, it is difficult to show why physicists should be sufficiently interested in the quantity $\mathbf{F} \cdot \mathbf{D}$ to give it a name. The fact is that, by making certain manipulations on the Newtonian equation of motion of a particle, namely $\mathbf{F} = m\mathbf{a}$, we can derive from it, for the case of a constant force, the scalar equation,

$$\mathbf{F} \cdot \mathbf{D} = \tfrac{1}{2}mv^2 - \tfrac{1}{2}mv_0^2$$

where v and v_0 are the magnitudes of the velocities of the particle at the end and the beginning of the displacement. [A more general equation, involving integration, results when **F** is not constant.] Because this equation is a mathematically simple consequence of the equation of motion and has various pleasant properties, it takes on important physical significance. Accordingly, physicists give names to the quantities therein. They call $\tfrac{1}{2}mv^2$ the *kinetic energy* of the particle, and, as we have already said, $\mathbf{F} \cdot \mathbf{D}$ the work done by **F** in the displacement **D**. This enables them to state the equation in words: the work done by the force is equal to the change it produces in the kinetic energy of the particle.

Exercise 2.6 A constant force **F** of magnitude F makes 45° with the x-axis. If it acts on a particle moving along the x-axis through a distance D, what is the work done?

Exercise 2.7 Prove that if, in Exercise 2.6, **F** had been perpendicular to the x-axis, the work done would have been zero.

Exercise 2.8 Show that if two constant forces $\mathbf{F}_1$ and $\mathbf{F}_2$ act on a particle, the work done by their resultant is the sum of the work done by $\mathbf{F}_1$ and the work done by $\mathbf{F}_2$.

Exercise 2.9 A constant force having components $(\mathbf{F}_x, 0, 0)$ acts on a particle that undergoes a displacement with components $(D_x, 0, 0)$, all components being relative to **i**, **j**, and **k**. What is the work done by the force?

Exercise 2.10 The same as Exercise 2.9, but with the force having components (F_x, F_y, F_z). [*Ans.* $F_x D_x$.]

Exercise 2.11 Show that the work done by a constant force **F** acting on a particle that moves through a displacement **D** can be regarded as the product of the magnitude of **F** and the length of the projection of **D** on the line of action of **F**.

3. SCALAR PRODUCTS AND UNIT ORTHOGONAL TRIADS

Using Equations (2.6) and (2.5), we have

$$\begin{aligned}(\mathbf{A} + \mathbf{B})\cdot(\mathbf{U} + \mathbf{V}) &= \mathbf{A}\cdot(\mathbf{U} + \mathbf{V}) + \mathbf{B}\cdot(\mathbf{U} + \mathbf{V}) \\ &= \mathbf{A}\cdot\mathbf{U} + \mathbf{A}\cdot\mathbf{V} + \mathbf{B}\cdot\mathbf{U} + \mathbf{B}\cdot\mathbf{V},\end{aligned}$$

and by repeated application of the same maneuvers, we see that a dot product of the type $(\mathbf{A} + \mathbf{B} + \ldots)\cdot(\mathbf{U} + \mathbf{V} + \ldots)$ is equal to the sum of all the individual dot products of each member of the first parenthesis with each member of the second.

Now consider two vectors **U** and **V** expressed in terms of their components relative to a unit orthogonal triad **i**, **j**, and **k**:

$$\mathbf{U} = U_x\mathbf{i} + U_y\mathbf{j} + U_z\mathbf{k} \tag{3.1}$$

$$\mathbf{V} = V_x\mathbf{i} + V_y\mathbf{j} + V_z\mathbf{k}. \tag{3.2}$$

How do we find the value of $\mathbf{U}\cdot\mathbf{V}$ in terms of the components? We could draw a diagram and work out the projection of **V** on **U** using a zigzag path. But there is an algebraic method that gives the result without any appeal to zigzag paths or even to a diagram, though, in fact, it is basically the same method.

We begin by noting that, from the definition of the scalar product, since the vectors **i**, **j**, and **k** have unit magnitude,

$$\left.\begin{aligned}\mathbf{i}\cdot\mathbf{i} = \mathbf{j}\cdot\mathbf{j} = \mathbf{k}\cdot\mathbf{k} = 1, \\ \mathbf{j}\cdot\mathbf{k} = \mathbf{k}\cdot\mathbf{i} = \mathbf{i}\cdot\mathbf{j} = 0, \\ \mathbf{k}\cdot\mathbf{j} = \mathbf{i}\cdot\mathbf{k} = \mathbf{j}\cdot\mathbf{i} = 0.\end{aligned}\right\} \tag{3.3}$$

We now write,

$$\mathbf{U}\cdot\mathbf{V} = (U_x\mathbf{i} + U_y\mathbf{j} + U_z\mathbf{k})\cdot(V_x\mathbf{i} + V_y\mathbf{j} + V_z\mathbf{k}),$$

and use the distributive law just discussed. There will be nine individual terms in the distributed product on the right, since each of the first three must multiply each of the second three. Of these nine terms, six will vanish because of the relations (3.3): for example, the term $(U_x\mathbf{i})\cdot(V_y\mathbf{j})$ equals $U_x V_y \mathbf{i}\cdot\mathbf{j}$ and this vanishes because $\mathbf{i}\cdot\mathbf{j} = 0$. Typical of the remaining three terms is $(U_x\mathbf{i})\cdot(V_x\mathbf{i})$ which equals $U_x V_x \mathbf{i}\cdot\mathbf{i}$, or just $U_x V_x$ since $\mathbf{i}\cdot\mathbf{i} = 1$. So we find in the end the neat-looking and powerful formula:

$$\mathbf{U}\cdot\mathbf{V} = U_x V_x + U_y V_y + U_z V_z. \tag{3.4}$$

Exercise 3.1 In addition to the distributive law, we used the fact that $(U_x\mathbf{i})\cdot(V_x\mathbf{i}) = U_x V_x \mathbf{i}\cdot\mathbf{i}$, etc. Note that this is obviously valid.

In particular, using Equation (2.4), we see from this that

$$V^2 = \mathbf{V}\cdot\mathbf{V} = V_x^2 + V_y^2 + V_z^2, \tag{3.5}$$

a result we already knew. Also, if **U** and **V** are perpendicular, $\cos\theta$ will be zero and therefore $\mathbf{U}\cdot\mathbf{V}$ will be zero so that we have this condition for perpendicularity:

$$U_x V_x + U_y V_y + U_z V_z = 0. \tag{3.6}$$

Exercise 3.2 Find the value of $\mathbf{U}\cdot\mathbf{V}$ if $\mathbf{U} = 2\mathbf{i} + 3\mathbf{j} - \mathbf{k}$ and $\mathbf{V} = 3\mathbf{i} + 4\mathbf{j} + 2\mathbf{k}$.

Exercise 3.3 Find the value of $\mathbf{U}\cdot\mathbf{V}$ if $\mathbf{U} = 4\mathbf{i} + 2\mathbf{j} - \mathbf{k}$ and $\mathbf{V} = 3\mathbf{i} - 5\mathbf{j} + 2\mathbf{k}$, and so show that **U** and **V** are perpendicular. [Imagine trying to prove this without the aid of Equation (3.4).]

Exercise 3.4 Do Exercises (2.9) and (2.10) using Equation (3.4).

Exercise 3.5 For what value of x will $3\mathbf{i} - 2\mathbf{j} + 3\mathbf{k}$ and $x\mathbf{i} - 2\mathbf{j} + 2\mathbf{k}$ be perpendicular?

Exercise 3.6 In Exercise 3.2, find the values of U and V, and thus, using Equation (2.3), show that for these vectors, $\cos\theta = 16/\sqrt{14}\sqrt{29}$.

Exercise 3.7 Show that when **U** and **V** are vectors of unit magnitude, Equation (3.4) is just $\cos\theta = ll' + mm' + nn'$ in disguise. Then compare this method of derivation with the previous zigzag method and see if you can trace out the underlying identity of the two methods.

From Equations (2.3) and (3.4) we see that

$$UV\cos\theta = U_x V_x + U_y V_y + U_z V_z,$$

so that

$$\cos\theta = \frac{U_x V_x + U_y V_y + U_z V_z}{UV}. \tag{3.7}$$

Compare this with Exercise (3.7).

Exercise 3.8 Using Equations (3.5) and (3.7), find $\cos\theta$ for the vectors $2\mathbf{i} + \mathbf{j} + \mathbf{k}$ and $3\mathbf{i} + 2\mathbf{j} + 2\mathbf{k}$. [*Ans.* $10/\sqrt{6}\sqrt{17}$.]

Exercise 3.9 Find the angle (not just its cosine) between $\mathbf{j} + \mathbf{k}$ and $\mathbf{i} + \mathbf{k}$, and draw a diagram showing the two vectors in relation to **i**, **j**, and **k**. [Note the bearing of this exercise on the following one.]

Exercise 3.10 From a vertex, O, of a cube, diagonals are drawn of the three square faces that meet at O. Prove that these diagonals make angles of 60° with each other. [While this may seem like an excellent demonstration of the power of the formula (3.5), the angles are easily found by ordinary geometry. Find them in that way too.]

Exercise 3.11 Prove that the vectors $\mathbf{i}, \mathbf{j} + \mathbf{k}$, and $\mathbf{i} + \mathbf{j} + \mathbf{k}$ are coplanar, and find the cosines of the angles between them. Also draw an appropriate diagram involving a cube, and from it check the angle between $\mathbf{i}$ and $\mathbf{j} + \mathbf{k}$ and the fact that the three vectors are coplanar. [To see without the diagram that the vectors are coplanar, note that one is the resultant of the other two.]

Exercise 3.12 Would Equation (3.4) be valid if (U_x, U_y, U_z) and (V_x, V_y, V_z) had been the components of $\mathbf{U}$ and $\mathbf{V}$ relative to a reference frame defined by general base vectors $\mathbf{e}_x$, $\mathbf{e}_y$, and $\mathbf{e}_z$? [This is probably the nastiest question in the book. According to all that has been said here, the answer is *no*, so give yourself full credit if that is your answer. However, there is more to the concept of a scalar product than we are in a position to explain here, and in a significant sense it could actually be correct to say that Equation (3.4) is valid in all reference frame.]

Let us derive Equation (6.2) of Chapter 3 by using scalar products. Here is the relevant part of the diagram:

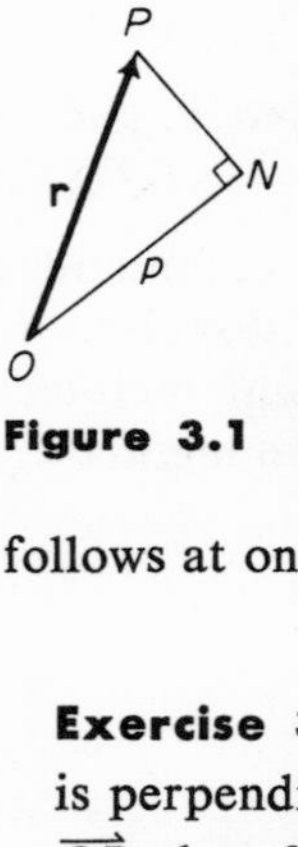

Figure 3.1

Denote by $\mathbf{r}$ the position vector of a general point P on the plane through N that is perpendicular to ON. Denote the unit vector along ON by $\mathbf{n}$. Then, since the length of the projection of OP on ON is p, we have

$$\mathbf{r} \cdot \mathbf{n} = p, \tag{3.8}$$

which is the required equation of the plane. To put it in the less compact, nonvectorial form, we note that $\mathbf{r}$ has components (x, y, z) and the components of the unit vector $\mathbf{n}$ are just the direction cosines (l, m, n) of the normal to the plane. It follows at once that

$$lx + my + nz = p.$$

Exercise 3.13 Derive this equation by expressing the fact that PN is perpendicular to ON. [*Hint*. The displacement $\overrightarrow{PN}$ is given by $\overrightarrow{ON} - \overrightarrow{OP}$; therefore, the perpendicularity can be expressed as $\overrightarrow{ON} \cdot (\overrightarrow{ON} - \overrightarrow{OP}) = 0$. This gives $\overrightarrow{ON} \cdot \overrightarrow{OP} = \overrightarrow{ON} \cdot \overrightarrow{ON}$. Now use the fact that $\overrightarrow{ON}$ and $\overrightarrow{OP}$ have components (lp, mp, np) and (x, y, z).]

Equation (3.7) for $\cos\theta$ can be used to obtain proofs of familiar formulas in trigonometry and two-dimensional analytical geometry. By way of orientation do this exercise first.

Exercise 3.14 Prove that the vectors $\mathbf{i} + 3\mathbf{j}$ and $4\mathbf{i} + 2\mathbf{j}$ make 45°

with each other. [Note that these vectors are in the xy-plane and can thus be regarded as belonging to two-dimensional analytical geometry in that plane. Note, too, how powerful the $\cos\theta$ formula is by contemplating the problem of trying to prove that the angle is 45° using only the methods of ordinary geometry. Draw the diagram and see for yourself.]

We shall now derive the well-known condition in two-dimensional analytical geometry that two lines be perpedicular. We recall that the slope of a line is defined as the tangent of the angle it makes with the x-axis, and that it is usually denoted by m (which, of course, is not to be confused with the m denoting a direction cosine). If a line in the xy-plane makes an angle α with the x-axis, its slope is given by $m = \tan\alpha$, and its direction cosines are easily seen to be $\cos\alpha$, $\sin\alpha$, and 0. Consider two lines making angles α and α' with the x-axis, and having slopes m and m'. We have, for perpendicularity, by Equation (3.6)

$$\cos\alpha\cos\alpha' + \sin\alpha\sin\alpha' = 0.$$

Divide this by $\cos\alpha\cos\alpha'$ and we find that $1 + mm' = 0$, or

$$mm' = -1,$$

showing that the slopes are negative reciprocals.

Exercise 3.15 Using the scalar product, derive the well-known trigonometric formula $\cos(A - B) = \cos A\cos B + \sin A\sin B$. [Consider the direction cosines of two lines in the xy-plane making angles A and B with the x-axis, and note that the angle between them is $A - B$.]

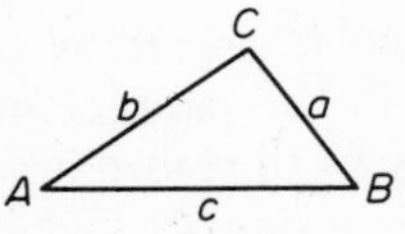

It is possible to derive the so-called law of cosines by means of the scalar product. In triangle ABC let the sides be of length a, b, and c as shown. Using displacements, we have $\overrightarrow{BC} = \overrightarrow{AC} - \overrightarrow{AB}$. So,

$$\begin{aligned} BC^2 &= \overrightarrow{BC}\cdot\overrightarrow{BC} = (\overrightarrow{AC} - \overrightarrow{AB})\cdot(\overrightarrow{AC} - \overrightarrow{AB}) \\ &= \overrightarrow{AC}\cdot\overrightarrow{AC} - 2\overrightarrow{AB}\cdot\overrightarrow{AC} + \overrightarrow{AB}\cdot\overrightarrow{AB} = AC^2 + AB^2 - 2(AB)(AC)\cos A. \end{aligned}$$

Therefore,

$$a^2 = b^2 + c^2 - 2bc\cos A.$$

5

VECTOR PRODUCTS. QUOTIENTS OF VECTORS

1. AREAS OF PARALLELOGRAMS

In the preceding chapter we noted that the quantity $UV \sin \theta$ gives the area of the parallelogram defined by the vectors **U** and **V**. We were therefore tempted to regard it as a "scalar product" of these vectors. We were discouraged from doing so when we found that this product would not obey the distributive law, but that $UV \cos \theta$ would. One of the purposes of this chapter is to rescue the quantity $UV \sin \theta$ from the danger of vectorial oblivion.

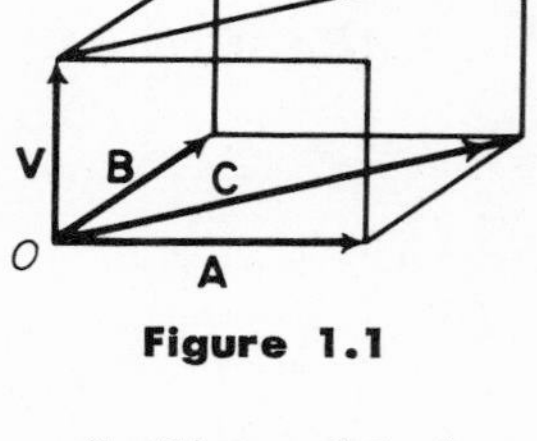

Figure 1.1

At this stage we do not know how to do this. But let us cross our fingers and agree to denote whatever it is we are seeking by the symbol $\mathbf{U} \times \mathbf{V}$ (to distinguish it from the $\mathbf{U} \cdot \mathbf{V}$ discussed in the preceding chapter) and to call it the *cross product* of **U** and **V**.

In Figure 1.1, the vectors **A**, **B**, and **C** are such that

$$\mathbf{C} = \mathbf{A} + \mathbf{B}. \tag{1.1}$$

To make our exploratory task easier, we consider first the special case in which vector **V** is perpendicular to the vectors **A**, **B**, and **C**.

By the symbol $\mathbf{V} \times \mathbf{A}$ we mean somehow to refer to the area of the parallelogram defined by **V** and **A**. [In the present special case, this and other parallelograms are actually rectangles, but let us use the word parallelogram nevertheless.] Here $\mathbf{V} \times \mathbf{A}$, the area of the parallelogram defined by **V** and **A**, is just VA. Similarly, the areas corresponding to the cross products $\mathbf{V} \times \mathbf{B}$ and $\mathbf{V} \times \mathbf{C}$ are VB and VC. We recall from the previous chapter that if we take $\mathbf{V} \times \mathbf{A}$ to mean just the area of the parallelogram defined by **V** and **A**, then $\mathbf{V} \times \mathbf{C} = \mathbf{V} \times (\mathbf{A} + \mathbf{B}) \neq \mathbf{V} \times \mathbf{A} + \mathbf{V} \times \mathbf{B}$. This is because the magnitude of $\mathbf{A} + \mathbf{B}$ is rarely equal to the sum of the magnitudes of **A** and **B**; that is, despite Equation (1.1) we have, in general,

$$C \neq A + B. \tag{1.2}$$

Exercise 1.1 What is wrong with the following argument? Since V, A, and B are scalars, we have, by ordinary algebra,

$$V(A + B) = VA + VB.$$

So if $\mathbf{V} \times \mathbf{A}$ stands for just VA, etc. we can write this as

$$\mathbf{V} \times (\mathbf{A} + \mathbf{B}) = \mathbf{V} \times \mathbf{A} + \mathbf{V} \times \mathbf{B}.$$

[*Hint.* Does the + on the left in the second equation mean the same thing as the other three +'s?]

One of the most important things in life is the ability to extract success from failure. This usually involves a seemingly contradictory combination of stubbornness and flexibility: one must be stubborn in one's determination to reach a solution, but highly flexible in seeking it.

Our failure above gives us an idea. We have, in effect, been multiplying Equation (1.2) by V. Why not work on Equation (1.1) instead? We shall then get

$$V\mathbf{C} = V(\mathbf{A} + \mathbf{B}) = V\mathbf{A} + V\mathbf{B}. \tag{1.3}$$

So if we agree to look on $\mathbf{V} \times \mathbf{A}$, for example, not as a *scalar* representing the area of the parallelogram defined by **V** and **A** but as a *vector* lying along **A** and having this area as magnitude, we shall be able to rewrite Equation (1.3) in the form

$$\mathbf{V} \times \mathbf{C} = \mathbf{V} \times (\mathbf{A} + \mathbf{B}) = \mathbf{V} \times \mathbf{A} + \mathbf{V} \times \mathbf{B}, \tag{1.4}$$

and apparently our troubles will be over—at least for the special case we are considering here.

But there is something unsatisfying and inelegant about representing the area of a parallelogram by a vector pointing along one of its sides. Why one side rather than the other? Why should $\mathbf{V} \times \mathbf{A}$, for instance, point along **A** rather than along **V**? Is there some way by which we can avoid playing favorites? We had better try choosing a neutral direction—a direction *perpendicular* to both **A** and **V**. How does Equation (1.4) fare if we think of $\mathbf{V} \times \mathbf{A}$ as having the same magnitude as before, but as pointing in a direction perpendicular to the plane of the parallelogram? Surprising as it may seem, Equation (1.4) survives. You may think this will be hard to prove. But actually it is obvious. For a glance at Figure 1.1 shows that the new $\mathbf{V} \times \mathbf{A}$, $\mathbf{V} \times \mathbf{B}$, and $\mathbf{V} \times \mathbf{C}$ are merely the old ones turned as a rigid body through 90° about $\mathbf{V}$ as an axis. Since Equation (1.3) holds for the **A**, **B**, and **C** in Figure 1.1, it obviously has to hold for the rotated vectors. Therefore Equation (1.4) still holds.

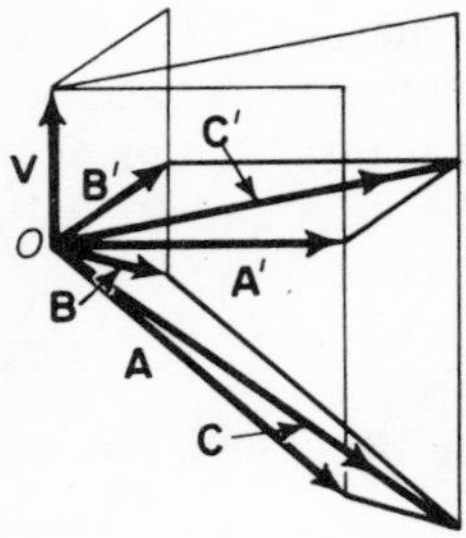

Figure 1.2

But we have been making things easy for ourselves by considering the special case in which **V** is perpendicular to **A**, **B**, and **C**. Will our luck hold when **V** is not perpendicular to them? It is easy to see that it will. Consider Figure 1.2, in which, though the plane of the vectors **A**, **B**, and **C** is not perpendicular to **V**, the plane of the vectors **A**′, **B**′, and **C**′ is; and the lines that look parallel to **V** are, in fact, parallel to **V**. The area of the (undrawn) parallelogram defined by **V** and **A** is equal to the area of the coplanar rectangle defined by **V** and **A**′. Therefore $\mathbf{V} \times \mathbf{A}' = \mathbf{V} \times \mathbf{A}$. Similarly $\mathbf{V} \times \mathbf{B}' = \mathbf{V} \times \mathbf{B}$, and $\mathbf{V} \times \mathbf{C}' = \mathbf{V} \times \mathbf{C}$, and that is about all we need. For the upper part of Figure 1.2 apes Figure 1.1, with **A**′, **B**′, and **C**′ replacing the **A**, **B**, and **C** in Figure 1.1. So relation (1.4) holds with **A**′, **B**′, and **C**′ replacing **A**, **B**, and **C**, and therefore, by the above equalities, it holds without the primes too, even though the present **A**, **B**, and **C** are not perpendicular to **V**.

Exercise 1.2 Go through the above proof for the special case in which **V**, **A**, **B**, and **C** are all coplanar, making the necessary adjustments in the diagram. [Since $\mathbf{V} \times \mathbf{A}$, $\mathbf{V} \times \mathbf{B}$, $\mathbf{V} \times \mathbf{C}$ have the same direction, Equation (4.1) reduces to a relation between the areas of three parallelograms in a plane. These areas are given by the products of a common base **V** with three altitudes the sum of the lengths of two of which is easily shown to be equal to the length of the third.]

What specially pleases us here is that when we look at the way Equation (1.4) was obtained, we see that it plays a dual role. Not only does it show that the distributive law is valid, but it also shows in what way we can regard the new $\mathbf{V} \times \mathbf{A}$ and $\mathbf{V} \times \mathbf{B}$ as combining according to the parallelogram law: if **C** is the vectorial resultant of **A** and **B**, then $\mathbf{V} \times \mathbf{C}$ will be the vectorial resultant of $\mathbf{V} \times \mathbf{A}$ and $\mathbf{V} \times \mathbf{B}$. We begin to sense that despite the change to the perpendicular direction, cross products can still be regarded as vectors. But what about the combination not of $\mathbf{V} \times \mathbf{A}$ and $\mathbf{V} \times \mathbf{B}$ but of, say, $\mathbf{L} \times \mathbf{M}$ and $\mathbf{R} \times \mathbf{S}$, in which there is no common letter, the vectors **L**, **M**, **R**, and **S**, all starting at O? Our luck still holds. we can reduce this to the simpler case quite easily as follows. Let the plane defined by **L** and **M** cut the plane defined by **R** and **S** in the line λ. Take any nonzero vector **V** along λ. Then we can always find a vector **A** in the plane of **L** and **M** such that the area of the parallelogram defined by **V** and **A** is the same as that of the parallelogram defined by **L** and **M**. Since **V** and **A** lie in the same plane as **L** and **M**, the quantity $\mathbf{V} \times \mathbf{A}$ will be the same as $\mathbf{L} \times \mathbf{M}$. Similarly we can replace $\mathbf{R} \times \mathbf{S}$ by $\mathbf{V} \times \mathbf{B}$ *where* $\mathbf{V}$ *is the same* $\mathbf{V}$ *as before.* Consequently $\mathbf{L} \times \mathbf{M} + \mathbf{R} \times \mathbf{S}$ reduces to the case $\mathbf{V} \times \mathbf{A} + \mathbf{V} \times \mathbf{B}$ that we have already considered.

Exercise 1.3 In the above, if $\mathbf{L}$ and $\mathbf{M}$ were $\mathbf{i}$ and $\mathbf{j}$ respectively, and $\mathbf{V}$ was $\mathbf{i} + \mathbf{j}$, what would $\mathbf{A}$ be? [*Ans.* It could be $\mathbf{i}$. It also could be $\mathbf{j}$. Or $\frac{1}{2}\mathbf{j} - \frac{1}{2}\mathbf{i}$. And there are infinitely many other possibilities. The fact is that the $\mathbf{A}$ and $\mathbf{B}$ above were by no means unique.]

Exercise 1.4 Deduce from the above discussion that $\mathbf{L} \times \mathbf{M} + \mathbf{R} \times \mathbf{S} = \mathbf{R} \times \mathbf{S} + \mathbf{L} \times \mathbf{M}$.

By now we may be fairly well convinced that we can regard these cross products as vectors. But a minor trouble comes to mind: which way should $\mathbf{V} \times \mathbf{A}$ point? There are two opposite directions perpendicular to a given plane. If we are not consistent in our choice of direction, we shall lose Equation (1.4).

Exercise 1.5 Why?

We shall therefore have to adopt a special convention. Let us agree to say that $\mathbf{U}$, $\mathbf{V}$, and $\mathbf{U} \times \mathbf{V}$, in that order, form a right-handed system. This then takes care of the problem. But it does so at a price:

$$\mathbf{U} \times \mathbf{V} = -\mathbf{V} \times \mathbf{U}. \qquad (1.5)$$

Exercise 1.6 Prove Equation (1.5). [Note that, by the convention, $\mathbf{V}$, $\mathbf{U}$, and $\mathbf{V} \times \mathbf{U}$, in that order, must also form a right-handed system; but the third member of a right-handed triad starting with $\mathbf{V}$, $\mathbf{U}$ points in the opposite direction to that of a triad starting with $\mathbf{U}$, $\mathbf{V}$.]

We are now ready for the official definition: *the cross product* $\mathbf{U} \times \mathbf{V}$ *denotes a vector having magnitude* $UV \sin \theta$ *and pointing in a direction perpendicular to* $\mathbf{U}$ *and* $\mathbf{V}$ *in such a way as to make* $\mathbf{U}$, $\mathbf{V}$, *and* $\mathbf{U} \times \mathbf{V}$, *in that order, a right-handed system.* The cross product is often also called the *vector product.* [We shall have more to say about the right-handed system later.]

Perhaps you think that this standard definition is long overdue. But let us go into this matter of the vector product with our eyes open. We have indeed shown how cross products can be regarded as vectors. But, as you have doubtless uneasily realized, in so doing we have had to agree to some curious things about the way areas are to be regarded as combining. We shall have to look into this in more detail later. Meanwhile, let us learn how to work with vector products.

Exercise 1.7 Show that $\mathbf{A} \times \mathbf{A} = 0$, and that $\mathbf{A} \times (\alpha\mathbf{A}) = 0$, where α is a scalar.

Exercise 1.8 If $\mathbf{U}$ is of magnitude 3 and points horizontally due east, and $\mathbf{V}$ is of magnitude 5 and points vertically upward, describe the vector $\mathbf{U} \times \mathbf{V}$. [*Ans.* Magnitude 15, and pointing—well, let's see—due south—I hope!]

Exercise 1.9 If $\mathbf{U}$ is of magnitude 8 and points horizontally due west, and $\mathbf{V}$ is of magnitude 7 and points horizontally 45° north of west, describe the vector $\mathbf{U} \times \mathbf{V}$.

Exercise 1.10 By applying Equation (1.5) to Equation (1.4) show that

$$(\mathbf{A} + \mathbf{B}) \times \mathbf{V} = \mathbf{A} \times \mathbf{V} + \mathbf{B} \times \mathbf{V}. \tag{1.6}$$

Exercise 1.11 Using Equations (1.4) and (1.6) show that

$$(\mathbf{A} + \mathbf{B}) \times (\mathbf{U} + \mathbf{V}) = \mathbf{A} \times \mathbf{U} + \mathbf{A} \times \mathbf{V} + \mathbf{B} \times \mathbf{U} + \mathbf{B} \times \mathbf{V}.$$

and generalize this to the case in which each parenthesis contains the sum of any number of vectors.

Exercise 1.12 Triangle ABC has sides of length a, b, and c. Using vector products, prove that $a/\sin A = b/\sin B = c/\sin C$. [*Hint.* Using displacements, we have $\overrightarrow{BC} + \overrightarrow{CA} + \overrightarrow{AB} = 0$. Take the cross product of this with $\overrightarrow{BC}$, and use Equation (1.5). Then do the same with $\overrightarrow{CA}$.]

Exercise 1.13 Show that $(\mathbf{A} - \mathbf{B})\cdot(\mathbf{A} + \mathbf{B}) = A^2 - B^2$ and that $(\mathbf{A} - \mathbf{B}) \times (\mathbf{A} + \mathbf{B}) = 2\mathbf{A} \times \mathbf{B}$, and interpret these results geometrically by means of appropriate diagrams.

2. CROSS PRODUCTS OF i, j, AND k

From the definition of a vector product, since sin 0° = 0 and sin 90° = 1, and **i**, **j**, and **k** are unit vectors, we have for a right-handed unit orthogonal triad the important relations

$$\left.\begin{aligned} \mathbf{i} \times \mathbf{i} &= \mathbf{j} \times \mathbf{j} = \mathbf{k} \times \mathbf{k} = 0, \\ \mathbf{j} \times \mathbf{k} &= -\,\mathbf{k} \times \mathbf{j} = \mathbf{i}, \\ \mathbf{k} \times \mathbf{i} &= -\,\mathbf{i} \times \mathbf{k} = \mathbf{j}, \\ \mathbf{i} \times \mathbf{j} &= -\,\mathbf{j} \times \mathbf{i} = \mathbf{k}. \end{aligned}\right\} \tag{2.1}$$

These relations are worth comparing with the corresponding relations for dot products given in Equation (3.3) of the preceding chapter.

Exercise 2.1 If α and β are scalars, show from the definition of the cross product that $(\alpha\mathbf{i}) \times (\beta\mathbf{i}) = 0$, $(\alpha\mathbf{j}) \times (\beta\mathbf{k}) = \alpha\beta\mathbf{i}$, $(\alpha\mathbf{k}) \times (\beta\mathbf{j}) = -\,\alpha\beta\mathbf{i}$, etc., and in general that $(\alpha\mathbf{U}) \times (\beta\mathbf{V}) = \alpha\beta\, \mathbf{U} \times \mathbf{V}$.

Exercise 2.2 Using the relations (2.1), show that

$$2\mathbf{i} \times (3\mathbf{i} + 4\mathbf{j} + 5\mathbf{k}) = -\,10\mathbf{j} + 8\mathbf{k}.$$

Exercise 2.3 As in Exercise 2.2, find the components relative to **i**, **j**, and **k** of the vector $(U_x\mathbf{i}) \times (V_x\mathbf{i} + V_y\mathbf{j} + V_z\mathbf{k})$.

Exercise 2.4 Like Exercise 2.3 for $(U_x\mathbf{i} + U_y\mathbf{j}) \times (V_x\mathbf{i} + V_y\mathbf{j})$. Note that the result is perpendicular to **i** and **j**, and explain why this was to have been expected. [Note that, for example, $U_x\mathbf{i} + U_y\mathbf{j}$ lies in the same plane as **i** and **j**.]

Exercise 2.5 Using the scalar product, find the cosine of the angle between **i** and $\mathbf{i} + \mathbf{j} + \mathbf{k}$. Then, using the vector product, find the sine of this angle. Check that the sum of their squares comes to unity. [To find the sine, calculate the magnitudes of **i** and $\mathbf{i} + \mathbf{j} + \mathbf{k}$ and multiply by the unknown $\sin\theta$. The result must be equal to the magnitude of the cross product $\mathbf{i} \times (\mathbf{i} + \mathbf{j} + \mathbf{k})$. The sine comes to $\sqrt{2}/\sqrt{3}$ and the cosine to $1/\sqrt{3}$.]

Exercise 2.6 Like Exercise 2.5 for $\mathbf{i} + \mathbf{j}$ and $\mathbf{i} + \mathbf{j} + \mathbf{k}$.

Exercise 2.7 By drawing a cube and noting two congruent triangles, explain why the cosine in Exercise 2.5 equals the sine in Exercise 2.6.

3. COMPONENTS OF CROSS PRODUCTS RELATIVE TO i, j, AND k

If

$$\mathbf{U} = U_x\mathbf{i} + U_y\mathbf{j} + U_z\mathbf{k}, \tag{3.1}$$

$$\mathbf{V} = V_x\mathbf{i} + V_y\mathbf{j} + V_z\mathbf{k}, \tag{3.2}$$

we can find the components of $\mathbf{U} \times \mathbf{V}$ by much the same method we used for finding $\mathbf{U}\cdot\mathbf{V}$ under similar circumstances. We have

$$\mathbf{U} \times \mathbf{V} = (U_x\mathbf{i} + U_y\mathbf{j} + U_z\mathbf{k}) \times (V_x\mathbf{i} + V_y\mathbf{j} + V_z\mathbf{k}). \tag{3.3}$$

Of the nine terms that arise from the product on the right, three are zero, namely $U_xV_x\mathbf{i} \times \mathbf{i}$, $U_yV_y\mathbf{j} \times \mathbf{j}$, and $U_zV_z\mathbf{k} \times \mathbf{k}$, because of Equations (2.1). The other six terms fall naturally into three pairs. For example, $U_yV_z\mathbf{j} \times \mathbf{k}$ and $U_zV_y\mathbf{k} \times \mathbf{j}$ belong together because $\mathbf{j} \times \mathbf{k} = -\mathbf{k} \times \mathbf{j} = \mathbf{i}$. In fact, these two terms may be combined as $(U_yV_z - U_zV_y)\mathbf{i}$. Two other pairs may be similarly treated, and we ultimately find that

$$\mathbf{U} \times \mathbf{V} = (U_yV_z - U_zV_y)\mathbf{i} + (U_zV_x - U_xV_z)\mathbf{j} + (U_xV_y - U_yV_x)\mathbf{k}. \tag{3.4}$$

Exercise 3.1 Check that the other two pairs do yield the two terms written in Equation (3.4).

Comparing this formula with that for $\mathbf{U}\cdot\mathbf{V}$, we see that the products U_xV_x, U_yV_y, U_zV_z that survive in $\mathbf{U}\cdot\mathbf{V}$ are absent from $\mathbf{U} \times \mathbf{V}$, while the products U_xV_y, etc. that are absent from $\mathbf{U}\cdot\mathbf{V}$ are the ones that survive in $\mathbf{U} \times \mathbf{V}$. The formula for $\mathbf{U} \times \mathbf{V}$ is not as pleasant as the one for $\mathbf{U}\cdot\mathbf{V}$; but its structure is not at all as complicated as it seems, and writing it down from memory is a fairly simple matter. Note first that the coefficient of **i** does not contain U_x and V_x, the components along **i** of the original vectors; and similarly for **j** and **k**. Next note that if we take x, y, and z, in cyclic order (that is, $x \to y \to z \to x \cdots$, as would be the case if x, y, and z were written in a circle), then the positive terms have the suffixes in this order (when we write the components of the first vector first, as we would naturally do). The positive terms may thus be written down easily, and if gaps are left for the negative terms, we can fill them in later by simply reversing the order of the suffixes that appeared in the corresponding positive terms.

Exercise 3.2 Study the above. Then, *without looking at Equation* (3.4), fill in the missing terms in the following:

$$\mathbf{A} \times \mathbf{B} = (A_y B_z - \qquad)\,\mathbf{i} + (A_z B_x - \qquad)\,\mathbf{j} + (A_x B_y - \qquad)\,\mathbf{k}.$$

Exercise 3.3 Write the positive terms in the formula for $\mathbf{L} \times \mathbf{Q}$, leaving gaps for the negative terms. Then fill in the latter.

Exercise 3.4 Write the formula for $\mathbf{V} \times \mathbf{U}$ and verify that it is the negative of that for $\mathbf{U} \times \mathbf{V}$.

Exercise 3.5 Without looking at the full formula, write down the coefficient of $\mathbf{j}$ in $\mathbf{U} \times \mathbf{V}$ and that of $\mathbf{k}$ in $\mathbf{B} \times \mathbf{A}$.

There is another way of remembering how to write the formula for a vector product in terms of components. First write

$$\begin{array}{cccc} \mathbf{i} & \mathbf{j} & \mathbf{k} & \mathbf{i} \\ U_x & U_y & U_z & U_x \\ V_x & V_y & V_z & V_x . \end{array} \qquad (3.5)$$

[The arrows may be omitted once you are used to the method.] For the component of $\mathbf{U} \times \mathbf{V}$ along $\mathbf{i}$, consult the $\mathbf{j}$ and $\mathbf{k}$ columns, and form the two products indicated by the arrows, counting the downward products positive and the upward ones negative. For the coefficient of $\mathbf{j}$, do the same with the $\mathbf{k}$ and $\mathbf{i}$ columns (the third and fourth), and for the coefficient of $\mathbf{k}$ use the $\mathbf{i}$ and $\mathbf{j}$ columns (the first and second).

If you have studied determinants, you will already have realized that, formally,

$$\mathbf{U} \times \mathbf{V} = \begin{vmatrix} \mathbf{i} & \mathbf{j} & \mathbf{k} \\ U_x & U_y & U_z \\ V_x & V_y & V_z \end{vmatrix} \qquad (3.6)$$

and there in no reason why you should not find cross products by means of this formula.

Choose whichever method you find most congenial. When dealing with symbols having appropriate suffixes, I prefer the first since it lets one write down the formula or any part of it immediately without bothering with Equation (3.4), or schema (3.5), or Equation (3.6). In numerical problems involving $\mathbf{i}$, $\mathbf{j}$, and $\mathbf{k}$, we can use the distributive law and the relations (2.1). For example, to work out $(2\mathbf{i} + 3\mathbf{j} + \mathbf{k}) \times (3\mathbf{i} + 2\mathbf{j} + 5\mathbf{k})$, we first note that the $\mathbf{i} \times \mathbf{i}$, $\mathbf{j} \times \mathbf{j}$, and $\mathbf{k} \times \mathbf{k}$ terms will vanish. Then we group the $15\mathbf{j} \times \mathbf{k}$ and the $2\mathbf{k} \times \mathbf{j}$ to give $15\mathbf{i} - 2\mathbf{i}$ or $13\mathbf{i}$, and similarly for the other terms. The result is $13\mathbf{i} - 7\mathbf{j} - 5\mathbf{k}$.

Exercise 3.6 Show that $(\mathbf{i} + 2\mathbf{j} + 3\mathbf{k}) \times (4\mathbf{i} + 5\mathbf{j} + 6\mathbf{k}) = 3(-\mathbf{i} + 2\mathbf{j} - \mathbf{k})$.

Exercise 3.7 Show that $(\mathbf{i} - 2\mathbf{j} + 3\mathbf{k}) \times (-4\mathbf{i} + 5\mathbf{j} + 6\mathbf{k}) = -3(9\mathbf{i} + 6\mathbf{j} + \mathbf{k})$.

Exercise 3.8 Find the sine of the angle between $\mathbf{i} + \mathbf{j} + \mathbf{k}$ and $\mathbf{i} + 2\mathbf{j} + 3\mathbf{k}$. Check the answer by finding the cosine from the scalar product and verifying that the sum of the squares of the sine and cosine is unity. [*Ans.* $1/\sqrt{7}$, $\sqrt{6}/\sqrt{7}$, the signs being correct for $0° \leq \theta \leq 180°$.]

Exercise 3.9 Like Exercise 3.8 for $3\mathbf{i} + 4\mathbf{k}$ and $2\mathbf{i} - \mathbf{j} - 2\mathbf{k}$. [*Ans.* $\sqrt{221}/15$, $-2/15$]

Exercise 3.10 Show that $\mathbf{i} \cos \alpha + \mathbf{j} \sin \alpha$ is a vector of unit magnitude in the **ij**-plane, making an angle α with **i**. Then, by considering the cross product of this vector with a similar one making an angle β with **i**, derive the well-known trigonometrical formula $\sin(\beta - \alpha) = \sin \beta \cos \alpha - \cos \beta \sin \alpha$.

Exercise 3.11 If $\mathbf{W} = \mathbf{U} \times \mathbf{V}$, then **W** is perpendicular to both **U** and **V**. Consequently $\mathbf{W} \cdot \mathbf{U} = 0$ and $\mathbf{W} \cdot \mathbf{V} = 0$. Express these two equations in terms of the components of **U**, **V**, and **W**, and by solving them, show that the components of **W** must be in the ratio

$$(U_y V_z - U_z V_y):(U_z V_x - U_x V_z):(U_x V_y - U_y V_x).$$

4. TRIPLE PRODUCTS

In ordinary algebraic multiplication of scalars, the expression *uvw* has a definite meaning. The situation is different when we are dealing with scalar products or vector products of vectors. For example, $\mathbf{U} \cdot \mathbf{V} \cdot \mathbf{W}$ has no meaning at all: if we form $\mathbf{U} \cdot \mathbf{V}$ first we obtain a scalar, and we can not form a dot product of this scalar with **W**; nor are we any better off if we form, say, $\mathbf{V} \cdot \mathbf{W}$ first. With cross products the situation is different. Consider, as a simple case, the expression $\mathbf{i} \times \mathbf{j} \times \mathbf{j}$. If we first form the product $\mathbf{i} \times \mathbf{j}$ we obtain **k**, and since this is a vector, we can certainly form its cross product with the remaining **j**: the result is $-\mathbf{i}$. But if we had first formed the product $\mathbf{j} \times \mathbf{j}$ we would have obtained the result zero. Let us write this in symbols:

$$(\mathbf{i} \times \mathbf{j}) \times \mathbf{j} = \mathbf{k} \times \mathbf{j} = -\mathbf{i} \quad \text{but} \quad \mathbf{i} \times (\mathbf{j} \times \mathbf{j}) = \mathbf{i} \times 0 = 0.$$

We see from this that an expression like $\mathbf{U} \times \mathbf{V} \times \mathbf{W}$ is ambiguous, its value depending on whether we first form $\mathbf{U} \times \mathbf{V}$ or $\mathbf{V} \times \mathbf{W}$. In general,

$$(\mathbf{U} \times \mathbf{V}) \times \mathbf{W} \neq \mathbf{U} \times (\mathbf{V} \times \mathbf{W}), \tag{4.1}$$

a fact that we express by saying that vector products do not obey the *associative* law. Therefore, whenever we have dealings with a quantity like

$\mathbf{U} \times \mathbf{V} \times \mathbf{W}$, we have to include parentheses, as $(\mathbf{U} \times \mathbf{V}) \times \mathbf{W}$ or $\mathbf{U} \times (\mathbf{V} \times \mathbf{W})$, to show what we mean. Notice that Equation (4.1) preserved the order of the vectors **U**, **V**, and **W**. We are not concerned here with the changes of sign that could arise if we altered the order.

Exercise 4.1 Find the values of $(\mathbf{j} \times \mathbf{k}) \times \mathbf{k}$ and $\mathbf{j} \times (\mathbf{k} \times \mathbf{k})$.

Exercise 4.2 Find the values of $(\mathbf{i} \times \mathbf{j}) \times \mathbf{i}$ and $\mathbf{i} \times (\mathbf{j} \times \mathbf{i})$ and show that they happen to be equal.

Exercise 4.3 Find the values of all of the following that have meaning: $(\mathbf{i} + \mathbf{j} + \mathbf{k}) \times \mathbf{k}$, $(\mathbf{i}\cdot\mathbf{i}) \times \mathbf{j}$, $\mathbf{i}\cdot(\mathbf{i} \times \mathbf{j})$, $(\mathbf{i}\cdot\mathbf{i})\,\mathbf{j}$, $(\mathbf{i}\cdot\mathbf{i})\cdot\mathbf{j}$, $(\mathbf{i} - \mathbf{j})\cdot(\mathbf{i} + \mathbf{j})$, $[(\mathbf{i} - \mathbf{j}) \times (\mathbf{i} + \mathbf{j})] \times \mathbf{i}$, $[(\mathbf{i} - \mathbf{j}) \times (\mathbf{i} + \mathbf{j})] \times \mathbf{k}$, $(\mathbf{i}\cdot\mathbf{i})(\mathbf{i}\cdot\mathbf{i})$, $(\mathbf{i}\cdot\mathbf{i}) \times (\mathbf{i}\cdot\mathbf{i})$, $(2\mathbf{i})\cdot(3\mathbf{i})$. [Three are meaningless.]

Exercise 4.4 Find the values of $[(\mathbf{i} + \mathbf{k}) \times \mathbf{j}] \times (\mathbf{i} + \mathbf{k})$ and $(\mathbf{i} + \mathbf{k}) \times [\mathbf{j} \times (\mathbf{i} + \mathbf{k})]$ and show that they happen to be equal.

Exercise 4.5 From Exercises, 4.2 and 4.4 we begin to suspect that $(\mathbf{U} \times \mathbf{V}) \times \mathbf{U} = \mathbf{U} \times (\mathbf{V} \times \mathbf{U})$. Using Equation (1.5) twice, prove that this relation is indeed true. [Use Equation (1.5) once on $(\mathbf{U} \times \mathbf{V})$ and then on the pair $(\mathbf{U} \times \mathbf{V}) \times \mathbf{U}$.]

Exercise 4.6 Show that $\mathbf{i}\cdot(\mathbf{j} \times \mathbf{k}) = (\mathbf{i}\cdot\mathbf{j}) \times \mathbf{k} = \mathbf{i} \times (\mathbf{j}\cdot\mathbf{k}) = (\mathbf{i} \times \mathbf{j})\cdot\mathbf{k} = 1$. [This is not a coincidence. It is a special case of what we are about to prove.]

Consider the parallelepiped defined by three vectors **U**, **V**, and **W** having a common starting point O.

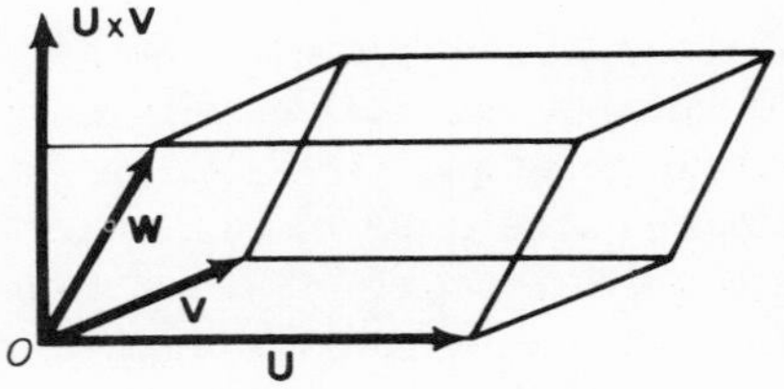

The cross product $\mathbf{U} \times \mathbf{V}$ is perpendicular to the parallelogram defined by **U** and **V**, and its magnitude is equal to the area of the parallelogram. To find the volume of the parallelepiped, we multiply the area of the base by the altitude. But the altitude is $W \cos\theta$, where θ is the angle that **W** makes with the normal to the base. The vector $\mathbf{U} \times \mathbf{V}$ happens conveniently to be normal to the base. Therefore $(\mathbf{U} \times \mathbf{V})\cdot\mathbf{W}$ will give us the volume of the parallelepiped, provided **U**, **V**, and **W** form a right-handed set. If not, $(\mathbf{U} \times \mathbf{V})\cdot\mathbf{W}$ will come out negative and will give minus the volume. Since the dot product is commutative, $(\mathbf{U} \times \mathbf{V})\cdot\mathbf{W} = \mathbf{W}\cdot(\mathbf{U} \times \mathbf{V})$. Also, since the expression $\mathbf{U} \times (\mathbf{V}\cdot\mathbf{W})$ would be nonsense, we can omit the parentheses in $(\mathbf{U} \times \mathbf{V})\cdot\mathbf{W}$ and write it without ambiguity as $\mathbf{U} \times \mathbf{V}\cdot\mathbf{W}$.

It is clear that we could also find the volume using different base parallelograms, namely, those defined by **V** and **W**, and by **W** and **U** (note the order of this last). We thus have, for a right-handed set of vectors **U**, **V**, and **W**, the following seemingly formidable array of equalities which in fact tells us something simple:

Volume of parallelepiped defined by $\mathbf{U}$, $\mathbf{V}$, and $\mathbf{W} = \mathbf{U} \times \mathbf{V} \cdot \mathbf{W} = \mathbf{V} \times \mathbf{W} \cdot \mathbf{U} = \mathbf{W} \times \mathbf{U} \cdot \mathbf{V} = \mathbf{U} \cdot \mathbf{V} \times \mathbf{W} = \mathbf{V} \cdot \mathbf{W} \times \mathbf{U} = \mathbf{W} \cdot \mathbf{U} \times \mathbf{V} = -\mathbf{V} \times \mathbf{U} \cdot \mathbf{W} = -\mathbf{W} \times \mathbf{V} \cdot \mathbf{U} = -\mathbf{U} \times \mathbf{W} \cdot \mathbf{V} = -\mathbf{U} \cdot \mathbf{W} \times \mathbf{V} = -\mathbf{V} \cdot \mathbf{U} \times \mathbf{W} = -\mathbf{W} \cdot \mathbf{V} \times \mathbf{U}$. (4.2)

What these relations tell us is that when we form a triple product of vectors using one dot and one cross, it does not matter where we put the dot and cross (within reason, of course—we would not want them on another page, nor even like this: $\cdot\ \mathbf{UVW} \times$). Moreover, it does not matter whether we start with $\mathbf{U}$, or $\mathbf{V}$, or $\mathbf{W}$, just so long as we keep the letters in cyclic order. And if we should break the cyclic order, the only penalty would be a minus sign. Because of this flexibility, the six positive combinations in Equation (4.2) are often denoted by the single symbol $[\mathbf{UVW}]$.

Exercise 4.7 Rewrite a sampling of the relations (4.2) for the case of a left-handed set of vectors $\mathbf{U}$, $\mathbf{V}$, and $\mathbf{W}$. [$\mathbf{U} \times \mathbf{V} \cdot \mathbf{W}$ will now have a minus sign in front of it, and $\mathbf{V} \times \mathbf{U} \cdot \mathbf{W}$ a plus sign, for example. In practice, it is simplest to avoid left-handed sets $\mathbf{U}$, $\mathbf{V}$, and $\mathbf{W}$ by rearranging their order so as to form a right-handed set. If $\mathbf{U} \times \mathbf{V} \cdot \mathbf{W}$ comes out negative, we know that the set was left-handed. Let us assume in this section that our sets of vectors are right-handed. We shall have to look into the matter of handedness in more detail later.]

Exercise 4.8 Show by means of Equation (4.2) that the volume of the cube defined by $\mathbf{i}$, $\mathbf{j}$, and $\mathbf{k}$ is unity. Work it out several ways.

Exercise 4.9 Find the volume of the parallelepiped defined by $\mathbf{j} + \mathbf{k}$, $\mathbf{k} + \mathbf{i}$, and $\mathbf{i} + \mathbf{j}$. [Note how complicated this looks when one tries to prove the simple result geometrically by means of a diagram.]

Exercise 4.10 Show that $\mathbf{i} \times (\mathbf{i} + \mathbf{j}) \cdot (\mathbf{i} + \mathbf{j} + \mathbf{k}) = 1$. Interpret the result geometrically in connection with a cube of unit edge, and then prove the theorem geometrically. [Once you see it, the geometrical proof is easy. But it may take you some time to see it.]

Exercise 4.11 Find the volume of the parallelepiped defined by $\mathbf{i} + 2\mathbf{j} + 3\mathbf{k}$, $2\mathbf{i} + 3\mathbf{j} + 4\mathbf{k}$, and $\mathbf{i} + 3\mathbf{j} + \mathbf{k}$. [*Ans.* 4.]

Exercise 4.12 If you have studied determinants show that

$$\mathbf{U} \cdot \mathbf{V} \times \mathbf{W} = \begin{vmatrix} U_x & U_y & U_z \\ V_x & V_y & V_z \\ W_x & W_y & W_z \end{vmatrix}.$$

Exercise 4.13 What must be true geometrically of the three nonzero vectors $\mathbf{A}$, $\mathbf{B}$, and $\mathbf{C}$, all starting at O, if $[\mathbf{ABC}] = 0$?

Exercise 4.14 What must be true geometrically of the four nonzero vectors $\mathbf{A}$, $\mathbf{B}$, $\mathbf{C}$, and $\mathbf{D}$, all starting at O, if $(\mathbf{A} \times \mathbf{B}) \cdot (\mathbf{C} \times \mathbf{D}) = 0$? What if $(\mathbf{A} \times \mathbf{B}) \times (\mathbf{C} \times \mathbf{D}) = 0$?

Exercise 4.15 Show that [UVU] = 0. Using this and similar results, show that [(V + W)(W + U)(U + V)] = 2[UVW], and interpret this relation geometrically. [Compare Exercise 4.9.]

As an example of the use of Equation (3.4), consider the not altogether pleasant problem of working out a formula for $\mathbf{U} \times (\mathbf{V} \times \mathbf{W})$. The result is clearly a vector. Let us therefore concentrate on the **i** component. This will come from $U_y\mathbf{j}$ multiplying the **k** term in $\mathbf{V} \times \mathbf{W}$, and $U_z\mathbf{k}$ multiplying the **j** term in $\mathbf{V} \times \mathbf{W}$. So it is:

$$U_y(V_x W_y - V_y W_x) - U_z(V_z W_x - V_x W_z).$$

Two of the terms have V_x as a factor and two others have W_x. So we regroup this as:

$$V_x(U_y W_y + U_z W_z) - W_x(U_y V_y + U_z V_z).$$

Now we add $U_x V_x W_x - U_x V_x W_x$, which is zero, and obtain

$$V_x(U_x W_x + U_y W_y + U_z W_z) - W_x(U_x V_x + U_y V_y + U_z V_z),$$

which is the **i** component of $\mathbf{V}(\mathbf{U}\cdot\mathbf{W}) - \mathbf{W}(\mathbf{U}\cdot\mathbf{V})$ or $(\mathbf{U}\cdot\mathbf{W})\mathbf{V} - (\mathbf{U}\cdot\mathbf{V})\mathbf{W}$. By symmetry, the other components will fit the same scheme. So

$$\mathbf{U} \times (\mathbf{V} \times \mathbf{W}) = (\mathbf{U}\cdot\mathbf{W})\mathbf{V} - (\mathbf{U}\cdot\mathbf{V})\mathbf{W}. \tag{4.3}$$

Exercise 4.16 Work out the **j** component by the same method.

5. MOMENTS

In Chapter 2, in connection with a seesaw, we became acquainted with the idea of the moment of a force. We now extend the discussion to the three-dimensional case.

Consider a rigid body acted on by a force **F** at a point A in it as shown in Figure 5.1. Let O be a pivotal point in the body. [The point O need not be a pivotal point, nor need there be a rigid body. One can take moments about any point, with or without a rigid body connecting the point and the force. For example, one can take the moment about the center of the sun of a force acting on a planet. However, we shall more easily get the feel of what is going on if we think here of O as an actual pivot in a rigid body acted on by the force **F**.] The turning effect of the force **F** about O is measured by the product of its magnitude F and the perpendicular distance, p, between O and its line of action. Thus the magnitude of the moment of **F** about O is pF.

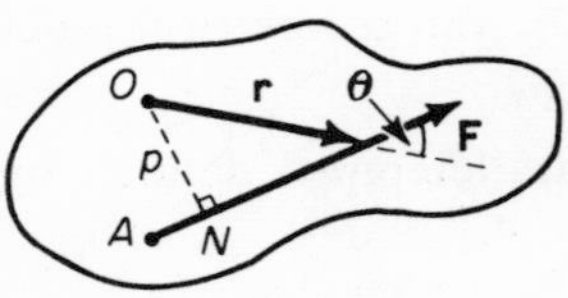

Figure 5.1

Now suppose we take *any* point P on the line of action of **F**. Let the position vector, r, of P relative to O make an angle θ with **F**, as shown. Then $p = r \sin\theta$. Therefore, the magnitude of the vector product $\mathbf{r} \times \mathbf{F}$, which is $rF \sin\theta$, is just pF, the magnitude of the moment of **F** about O.

The relation between $\mathbf{r} \times \mathbf{F}$ and the moment of $\mathbf{F}$ about O is even closer than this. It extends to direction as well as magnitude. For the effect of $\mathbf{F}$ is to turn the rigid body in such a way as not to tilt the plane containing O and $\mathbf{F}$; thus the effect is not just to turn the body "about O" but rather to turn it about an axis through O that is perpendicular to the plane of $\mathbf{r}$ and $\mathbf{F}$. So we see that the moment, or turning effect, of $\mathbf{F}$ about O is, in this sense, given both as to its magnitude and the direction of its axis by $\mathbf{r} \times \mathbf{F}$. Moreover, if we reversed the direction of $\mathbf{F}$, thus producing a moment of opposite sign, the vector product $\mathbf{r} \times \mathbf{F}$ would automatically mirror this change of sign since, by the right-hand convention, $\mathbf{r} \times \mathbf{F}$ would now point in the direction diametrically opposite to its former direction.

Apparently, then, we may take $\mathbf{r} \times \mathbf{F}$ as representative of the moment of $\mathbf{F}$ about O. But before we do this, one thing remains to be verified. The quantity $\mathbf{r} \times \mathbf{F}$ is a vector. Do moments combine according to the parallelogram law? The answer is yes. But it is not an automatic yes. Simply agreeing to represent moments by vector products of the type $\mathbf{r} \times \mathbf{F}$ gives us no guarantee that the physical turning effect of an $\mathbf{r}_1 \times \mathbf{F}_1$ and an $\mathbf{r}_2 \times \mathbf{F}_2$ together is the same as the turning effect of their vectorial resultant. That it *is* the same can be deduced from equations $\mathbf{F} = m\mathbf{a}$ which are based on experiment. It can also be inferred directly from experiment. We omit the details.

This parallelogram-law behavior of moments of forces is a far-reaching thing. Consider, for example, the rigid cube shown in Figure 5.2, which we shall assume has edges of unit length. Let the cube be pivoted at O and be acted on by two forces $\mathbf{F}_1$ and $\mathbf{F}_2$ as shown in Figure 5.2. What is the combined turning effect of the two forces? The forces act somewhat, but not entirely, against each other; and it is not easy to visualize offhand what sort of a twist they would tend to give to the cube when acting together. We can find their combined turning effect by forming the resultant of two cross products; a convenient way to do this is to use components and then stop visualizing while we perform some routine calculations.

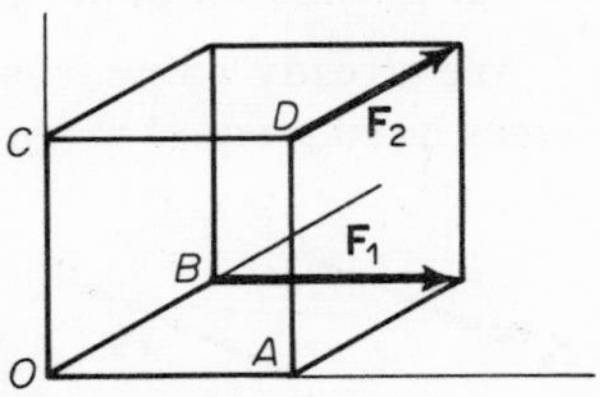

Figure 5.2

Let us introduce $\mathbf{i}$, $\mathbf{j}$, and $\mathbf{k}$ along OA, OB, and OC respectively. Then the moment vector of $\mathbf{F}_1$ is easily seen to be $-F_1\,\mathbf{k}$. [Why the minus?] To find the moment vector of $\mathbf{F}_2$ about O, we note that the position vector, $\mathbf{r}$, of the point D has components $(1, 0, 1)$, while the components of $\mathbf{F}_2$ are $(0, F_2, 0)$. So, by a standard procedure, we find that $\mathbf{r}_2 \times \mathbf{F}_2 = -\,\mathbf{F}_2\mathbf{i} + \mathbf{F}_2\mathbf{k}$. [The easiest procedure is to use the distributive law on $(\mathbf{i} + \mathbf{k}) \times (F_2\,\mathbf{j})$.] Thus the resultant moment is given by the vector $-F_2\mathbf{i} + (F_2 - F_1)\mathbf{k}$.

In particular, if the two forces have the same magnitudes, so that $F_1 = F_2$, we see that the resultant is just $-F_2\mathbf{i}$, a fact that may at first sight seem surprising. But if we look at the problem in a different way, this result becomes rather obvious. We simply ask ourselves what the combined turning effects of the forces are about the three axes OA, OB, and OC individually. (The turning effect of a force $\mathbf{F}$ about OA, for example, is measured by the moment about OA of the component of $\mathbf{F}$ perpendicular to OA.) About OA, the force $\mathbf{F}_1$ has zero moment but $\mathbf{F}_2$ has moment $-F_2$ because the perpendicular distance AD from OA to the line of action of $\mathbf{F}_2$ is unity. So the $\mathbf{i}$ component of the resultant moment is $-F_2$. About OB, the moments are both zero, because the line of action of $\mathbf{F}_1$ intersects OB, and $\mathbf{F}_2$ is parallel to OB. About OC, the moments are $-F_1$ and F_2, and when $F_1 = F_2$, the sum is zero.

Exercise 5.1 Explain how the distributive law of vector products justfies the second method above.

Exercise 5.2 Find the resultant moment about O in Figure 5.2 if $\mathbf{F}_1$ acts along CD and $\mathbf{F}_2$ along the diagonal BC. [*Ans.* $(F_2/\sqrt{2})\mathbf{i} + F_1\mathbf{j}$.]

Exercise 5.3 Like Exercise 5.2, but with $\mathbf{F}_2$ acting along the diagonal BD. [*Ans.* $-(F_2/\sqrt{3})\mathbf{i} + F_1\mathbf{j} - (F_2/\sqrt{3})\mathbf{k}$.]

Exercise 5.4 Show that if two nonzero forces act on a rigid body they will have zero resultant moment about a point O only if they lie in a plane through O.

Exercise 5.5 If the sum of the moments of n forces about a point O is zero, show that it will be zero about every other point, provided the resultant of the forces moved (as though they were free vectors) to act at a common point is zero. [Compare Exercise 6.6 of Chapter 2.]

We already know from Chapter 2 that a couple consists of two parallel forces having equal magnitudes and opposite directions but, in general, different lines of action. It is clear from the present discussion of the moment of a force about a point, that if P_1 and P_2 are any points on the respective lines of action of the forces $\mathbf{F}_1$ and $\mathbf{F}_2$ of a couple (these forces having equal magnitudes), the moment of the couple is given by the vector product $\overrightarrow{P_1P_2} \times \mathbf{F}_2$ (which is the same as $\overrightarrow{P_2P_1} \times \mathbf{F}_1$); and that if F is the common magnitude of the forces and d the perpendicular distance between them, the magnitude of the moment of the couple is Fd. Its direction, of course, is perpendicular to the plane of the couple.

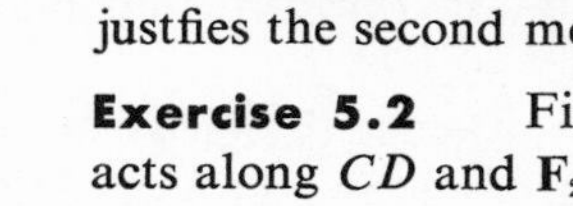

Figure 5.3

Exercise 5.6 Given a couple and any point O not necessarily in the plane of the forces comprising the couple, show that the resultant of the moments of the forces about O is equal to the moment vector of the couple. [Use the fact tht $\overrightarrow{OP_2} = \overrightarrow{OP_1} + \overrightarrow{P_1P_2}$.]

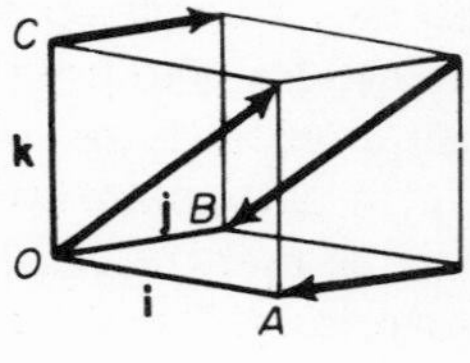

Exercise 5.7 Find the moment of the resultant couple of the two couples shown in the diagram, if all forces have magnitude 5 and the square

has sides 2 units long. [*Ans.* The individual couples have moments $-10\mathbf{i} - 10\mathbf{k}$, $-10\mathbf{i} + 10\mathbf{k}$, so their resultant is $-20\mathbf{i}$.]

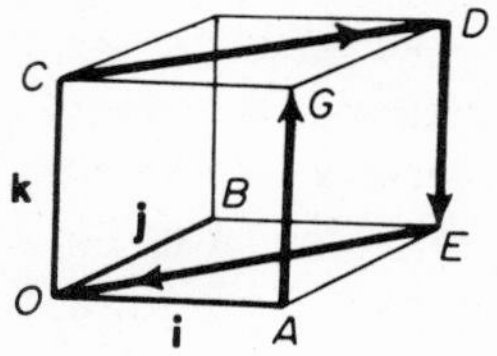

Exercise 5.8 Like Exercise 5.7 but with the couples as shown, the forces $\overrightarrow{AG}$ and $\overrightarrow{DE}$ having magnitudes of 2 lbs, and $\overrightarrow{CD}$ and $\overrightarrow{EO}$ $2\sqrt{2}$ lbs. [Why do we get the wrong answer if we argue that the three vectors $\overrightarrow{CD}$, $\overrightarrow{DE}$, and $\overrightarrow{EO}$ are together equivalent to the vector $\overrightarrow{CO}$ so that we have, in effect, just a single couple with forces along $\overrightarrow{CO}$ and $\overrightarrow{AG}$?]

Exercise 5.9 A force $\mathbf{F}$ acts at a point with position vector $\mathbf{r}$ relative to O. By introducing at O a pair of cancelling forces parallel to $\mathbf{F}$ and having the same magnitude as $\mathbf{F}$, show that the original force is equivalent to a parallel force of equal magnitude through O and a couple having a moment $\mathbf{r} \times \mathbf{F}$.

By applying the technique outlined in Exercise 5.9 to each force in succession, we can reduce any system of forces to a single resultant force at any point O and a single resultant couple. Let us denote the single force at O by $\mathbf{F}$ and the couple by $\mathbf{G}$. In general $\mathbf{F}$ and $\mathbf{G}$ will not be parallel. If we go to a new point P, the new force will be parallel to the old and, indeed, identical with it except for location. But the couple will in general be altered; for if the position vector of P relative to O is $\mathbf{r}$, there will be an additional couple $-\mathbf{r} \times \mathbf{F}$ arising from the change from O to P, so the resultant couple will be $\mathbf{G} - \mathbf{r} \times \mathbf{F}$. We therefore have a chance of finding a point P for which the resultant force and resultant couple of the system are parallel—in which case we say we have a *wrench*, this being the sort of influence one customarily exerts on a screwdriver. Let us see if we can find such a point P. We want $\mathbf{G} - \mathbf{r} \times \mathbf{F}$ to be parallel to $\mathbf{F}$. Therefore, we want $\mathbf{F} \times (\mathbf{G} - \mathbf{r} \times \mathbf{F}) = 0$, i.e.,

$$\mathbf{F} \times \mathbf{G} - \mathbf{F} \times (\mathbf{r} \times \mathbf{F}) = 0. \tag{5.1}$$

As it stands, this is not an easy equation to solve for $\mathbf{r}$. We therefore seek help from equation (4.3) which tells us that

$$\mathbf{F} \times (\mathbf{r} \times \mathbf{F}) = (\mathbf{F} \cdot \mathbf{F})\mathbf{r} - (\mathbf{F} \cdot \mathbf{r})\mathbf{F}.$$

This lets us write equation (5.1) in the form

$$\mathbf{F} \times \mathbf{G} - F^2\mathbf{r} + (\mathbf{F} \cdot \mathbf{r})\mathbf{F} = 0. \tag{5.2}$$

We are still not out of the woods. The next step is to decompose $\mathbf{r}$ into the sum of two vectors $\mathbf{n}$ and $\mathbf{p}$, $\mathbf{n}$ being parallel to $\mathbf{F} \times \mathbf{G}$ and thus normal to $\mathbf{F}$, and $\mathbf{p}$ being parallel to $\mathbf{F}$:

$$\mathbf{r} = \mathbf{n} + \mathbf{p}. \tag{5.3}$$

Then, since $\mathbf{F} \cdot \mathbf{n} = 0$, we have, from equation (5.2),

$$\mathbf{F} \times \mathbf{G} - F^2(\mathbf{n} + \mathbf{p}) + (\mathbf{F} \cdot \mathbf{p})\mathbf{F} = 0. \tag{5.4}$$

The component vectors of the vector 0 are zero in all directions. The component vectors of the resultant of the left hand side must therefore also be zero. Since $\mathbf{F} \times \mathbf{G}$ and $\mathbf{n}$ are perpendicular to $\mathbf{p}$ and $\mathbf{F}$, we see that we can extract two distinct equations from equation (5.4), one for the component vectors in the direction of $\mathbf{n}$, the other for the component vectors in the direction of $\mathbf{p}$. They are

$$\left.\begin{aligned} \mathbf{F} \times \mathbf{G} - F^2\mathbf{n} = 0 \\ -F^2\mathbf{p} + (\mathbf{F}\cdot\mathbf{p})\mathbf{F} = 0. \end{aligned}\right\} \tag{5.5}$$

So

$$\mathbf{n} = \frac{\mathbf{F} \times \mathbf{G}}{F^2}, \quad \mathbf{p} = \frac{(\mathbf{F}\cdot\mathbf{p})\mathbf{F}}{F^2}. \tag{5.6}$$

At first we are inclined to think that these equations (5.6), (5.3) fix the vector $\mathbf{r}$. But the second equation in (5.6) does not give $\mathbf{p}$; it gives only its direction —which we already knew was parallel to $\mathbf{F}$.

Exercise 5.10 Why does it give only the direction? [*Hint:* Try to find the magnitude of $\mathbf{p}$ from the equation and see what happens.]

Since Equation (5.1) will hold for all vectors $\mathbf{p}$ satisfying Equation (5.6), we see that instead of finding a single point P relative to which the forces of the system form a wrench, we have found a whole line of such points. This line is parallel to $\mathbf{F}$, and is called *Poinsot*'s *central axis*.

Exercise 5.11 The above mathematics breaks down if $\mathbf{F} = 0$. Does it matter? What could one say about the whole idea of searching for a central axis when $\mathbf{F} = 0$?

Exercise 5.12 Given one point relative to which a system of forces becomes a wrench, show that it is obvious that any point on the line through this point parallel to $\mathbf{F}$ will also be one relative to which the system is a wrench.

Exercise 5.13 Show that the magnitude of the resultant moment of the forces of a system is a minimum when the moment is taken relative to points on the central axis. [*Hint*: $\mathbf{F}$ does not change its magnitude or direction as one goes from point to point. $\mathbf{G}$ changes by $-\mathbf{r} \times \mathbf{F}$ which is perpendicular to $\mathbf{F}$. So $\mathbf{G}\cdot\mathbf{F}$ does not change value. For given $\mathbf{F}$ and $\mathbf{G}\cdot\mathbf{F}$, what angle should $\mathbf{G}$ make with $\mathbf{F}$ if G is to be a minimum?]

Exercise 5.14 Find the central axis of the forces in Figure 5.2. [We have $\mathbf{F} = F_1\mathbf{i} - F_2\mathbf{j}$, and, taking moments about O, $\mathbf{G} = -F_2\mathbf{i} + (F_2 - F_1)\mathbf{k}$. So $F^2 = F_1^2 + F_2^2$, $\mathbf{F} \times \mathbf{G} = -F_2(F_2 - F_1)\mathbf{i} - F_1(F_2 - F_1)\mathbf{j} - F_2^2\mathbf{k}$. Then calculate $\mathbf{n}$ using equation (5.6). Note how complicated the result is for even so simple a case as this.]

Exercise 5.15 Like Exercise 5.14 if the forces on the cube are those described in Exercise 5.2.

Exercise 5.16 Relative to a point O, a wrench pointing along $\mathbf{i}$ has

force and couple of magnitude 1 and 1. Another wrench, pointing along **j**, has force and couple of magnitude 1, 2 respectively. Find the resultant central axis. [*Ans.* A horizontal line through the point $(0, 0, \frac{1}{2})$ making 45° with the **i** and **j** directions.]

6. ANGULAR DISPLACEMENTS

If we rotate a rigid body about a fixed axis through an angle α radians, it undergoes an angular displacement. We can represent this angular displacement by means of an arrow-headed line segment of length α units (say inches) lying along the axis of rotation and pointing in the direction a right-handed corkscrew would move if similarly rotated.* Since the angular displacement has magnitude and direction and can be represented by an arrow-headed line segment, we begin to suspect that it behaves like a vector. Indeed, if we combine a rotation about a particular axis through an angle α radians with one about the same axis through an angle β radians, the resulting angular displacement is one of $\alpha + \beta$ radians about the axis, and this is just what we would obtain by combining the corresponding arrow-headed line segments according to the parallelogram law—the parallelogram, in this special case being, of course, squashed into a straight line. Again, if we combine a rotation about an axis through an angle α radians with a rotation about the same axis through an angle $-\alpha$ radians (which is through an angle α radians in the opposite direction and would thus pertain to an arrow-headed line segment pointing in a direction opposite to that of the line segment representing the original angular displacement), we end up with a zero angular displacement, and this result, too, we would get from the parallelogram law.

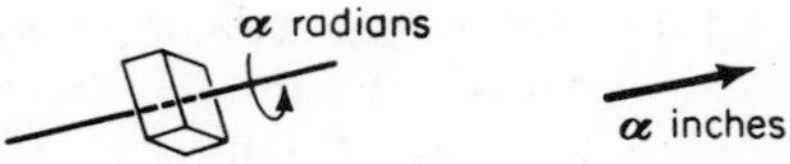

Figure 6.1

Add to all this our vectorial experiences not only with moments but even with such unlikely things as areas of parallelograms, and we begin to feel confident that angular displacements can be treated as vectors. It seems hardly necessary to check further whether the arrow-headed line segments representing angular displacements obey the parallelogram law.

But suppose we rotated the rigid body through α radians about an axis I_1, and then through $-\alpha$ radians through a different, but parallel axis I_2. Then the two angular displacements together would not leave the body in its original position. They would displace it, without rotation, to a new position.

Exercise 6.1 Check this assertion by considering the simple case of a rod AB in a plane, first rotating it about A and then rotating it through an equal angle in the opposite direction about the new position of B.

*Except, of course, that we were not contemplating any motion by the rigid body *along* the axis of rotation.

Evidently we have to tread carefully if we wish to regard angular displacements as vectors. Two ways of saving the situation seem open to us. One is to say that the resulting *rotation* above was zero, as predicted by the parallelogram law, and that the bodily displacement is not our present concern. The other is to say that then we combine angular displacements vectorially they must be angular displacements about the same axis. Clearly, the second is too drastic. If we combine only rotations having a common axis we shall never use the full parallelogram law but only the case in which the parallelogram is squashed into a line. While we would then be able to say correctly that rotations about a given axis behave like vectors, this would hardly be a worthwhile assertion.

We therefore try to combine the first possibility with a less stringent version of the second. We say that we want to look upon angular displacements not as free vectors but as bound (or at least sliding) vectors, and that we will limit ourselves to combining rotations about axes that have a common point. This immediately rules out the case of parallel axes that caused the trouble discussed earlier. Presumably, with this restriction, our luck will hold. Let us see.

Consider two rotations, each through $\pi/2$ radians,* about fixed perpendicular axes that, for convenience, we shall take to be the x-and y-axes of a three-dimensional rectangular Cartesian coordinate system. To simplify the discussion, take the rigid body to be a playing card, say the ace of spades. Place it face down in the position shown in Figure 6.2a. On rotating it about the x-axis through $\pi/2$ radians, we bring it into the position shown in Figure 6.2b. And on now rotating it about the y-axis through $\pi/2$ radians, we bring it finally to the position shown in Figure 6.2c.

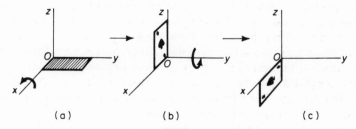

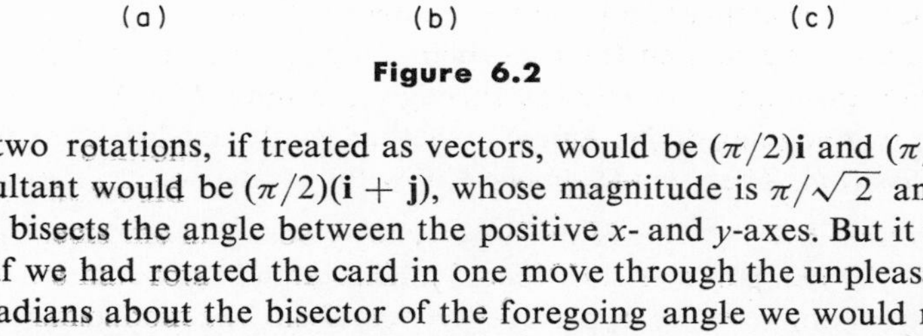

Figure 6.2

The two rotations, if treated as vectors, would be $(\pi/2)\mathbf{i}$ and $(\pi/2)\mathbf{j}$, and their resultant would be $(\pi/2)(\mathbf{i} + \mathbf{j})$, whose magnitude is $\pi/\sqrt{2}$ and whose direction bisects the angle between the positive x- and y-axes. But it is easy to see that if we had rotated the card in one move through the unpleasant angle $\pi/\sqrt{2}$ radians about the bisector of the foregoing angle we would not bring it into anything like the final position above. Therefore the arrow-headed line

*This is, of course, 90°. But we use radians here with an eye on the next section.

segments representing angular displacements have failed the parallelogram test, and they have done so even though we have limited ourselves to axes of rotation having a common point O. There is no avoiding the fact that we just cannot treat angular displacements about intersecting but nonidentical axes as vector quantities.

This fact becomes strikingly clear when we consider the effect of performing the above rotations in the reverse order. The sequence of positions of the card is shown in Figure 6.3, and the final position is quite different from

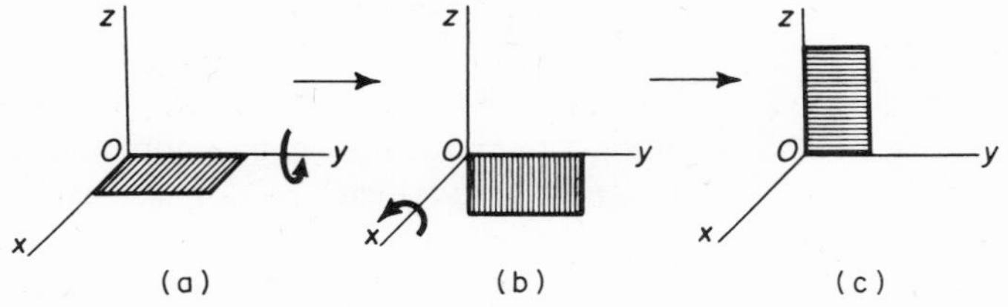

Figure 6.3

that in Figure 6.2. Thus, if we denote the rotations about the x- and y-axes respectively by X and Y, we see that the addition of angular displacements does not even obey the commutative law:

$$X + Y \neq Y + X.$$

Exercise 6.2 Starting with the card in the same position as above, rotate it first through $\pi/2$ radians about the y-axis and then through $\pi/2$ radians about the z-axis, and compare the resulting position with that obtained when these two rotations are perfomed in the reverse order. [The final positions are not the same.]

7. ANGULAR VELOCITY

Fresh from the chastening experience of the preceding section, let us consider a rigid body turning about a fixed axis at a constant rate of ω radians per second. Associated with the motion are a magnitude and a direction, the magnitude being ω and the direction that of the axis in, say, the right-hand corkscrew sense. Can it be properly regarded as a vector quantity?

Exercise 7.1 Place your bet: yes or no? [Whichever you choose, you will be surprised—either in this section or later.]

There are two ways of thinking of the motion. One is as a single over-all rotation; the other is as the set of motions of all the individual particles making up the rigid body. Let us think of it in the latter sense.

Take a fixed point O on the axis of rotation, and denote by $\mathbf{r}$ the position vector relative to O of a general point P of the rigid body. Draw PN perpendicular to the axis of rotation. The rotation of the body causes P to move in a circle perpendicular to the axis of rotation, the center of the circle being N. If $\mathbf{r}$ makes an angle θ with the axis, the radius of the circle, PN, is $r \sin \theta$. The speed of P is easily calculated. In any time t secs. the body turns through an angle of ωt radians. Therefore P traverses an arc length of $(\omega t)(r \sin \theta)$. Dividing this arc length by the time taken, namely t, we find that the speed of P is $\omega r \sin \theta$. [Note the advantage of using radians here. Had ω been given in deg./sec. the angle would have been $\omega t \pi/180$ radians, and the speed of P would have been given by the ugly expression $(\pi \omega r \sin \theta)/180$.]

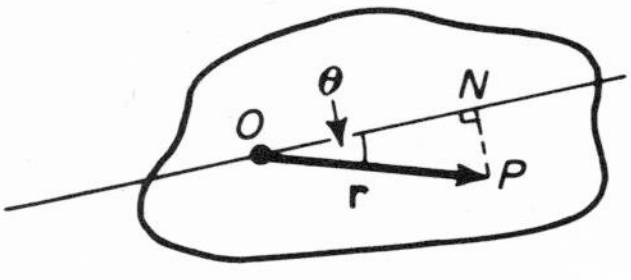

Figure 7.1

Though the speed of P is constant, its velocity is not. At each instant it lies along the tangent at P to the circle traversed by P, and its direction changes from instant to instant. The fact that the instantaneous velocity of P has a continually changing direction is a considerable complication. To avoid trouble with the changing direction in what follows, we would like to talk about what happens at a particular instant. But a genuine instant affords no time for anything at all to happen. It was precisely this sort of dilemma that the calculus was designed to overcome; but the dilemma is of such subtlety that even when Newton and Leibnitz succeeded in constructing a calculus that gave formalized mathematical procedures for dealing with it, a century was to pass before a significant beginning was made to put these procedures on an acceptable mathematical basis. Nevertheless, during that century enormous progress was made by means of the calculus.

Taking a hint from the pioneers, then, let us cross our fingers and try to get the feel of what is going on without striving for mathematical rigor. We ask ourselves whether we can regard the above motion of a rigid body as a vector. Let us see what happens if we think of it as a vector starting at O, call it *angular velocity*, and denote it by $\boldsymbol{\omega}$.

The first thing we observe is that we may now represent the instantaneous velocity, $\mathbf{v}$, of the point P by $\boldsymbol{\omega} \times \mathbf{r}$:

$$\mathbf{v} = \boldsymbol{\omega} \times \mathbf{r}. \tag{7.1}$$

Exercise 7.2 Verify Equation (7.1) considering both the magnitude and direction of $\mathbf{v}$, and noting that $\mathbf{r} \times \boldsymbol{\omega}$ would have given the wrong sign for $\mathbf{v}$.

Exercise 7.3 A rigid body is spinning about the z-axis with a constant angular speed of 10 radians/sec. At a particular instant, a point P in the body has coordinates (2, 2, 5). What is its velocity at that instant? [*Ans.* $10\mathbf{k} \times (2\mathbf{i} + 2\mathbf{j} + 5\mathbf{k})$, i. e., $20\mathbf{i} - 20\mathbf{j}$.]

Exercise 7.4 Like Exercise 7.3 if the body was rotating about a line through the origin whose positive direction makes equal acute angles with the positive directions of the axes. [*Ans.* $10\sqrt{3}\,\mathbf{i} - 10\sqrt{3}\,\mathbf{j}$. Note that the instantaneous velocity has a horizontal direction. Try to visualize the situation without thinking of vector products to see why the velocity of P at this instant has to be horizontal. You will then begin to realize the power of Equation (7.1).]

Now suppose that the rigid body was somehow subjected to two angular velocities $\boldsymbol{\omega}_1$ and $\boldsymbol{\omega}_2$ simultaneously, these having, in general, different axes but *axes with a common point O*. Since we are thinking of $\boldsymbol{\omega}_1$ and $\boldsymbol{\omega}_2$ as vectors starting at O, they will have a resultant, $\boldsymbol{\omega}$, also starting at O, that is given by:

$$\boldsymbol{\omega} = \boldsymbol{\omega}_1 + \boldsymbol{\omega}_2. \tag{7.2}$$

This equation is, of course, an expression of the fact that $\boldsymbol{\omega}_1$ and $\boldsymbol{\omega}_2$ yield $\boldsymbol{\omega}$ according to the parallelogram law.

Now $\boldsymbol{\omega}_1$ and $\boldsymbol{\omega}_2$ individually impart to P the respective velocities $\mathbf{v}_1$ and $\mathbf{v}_2$, these being given by:

$$\mathbf{v}_1 = \boldsymbol{\omega}_1 \times \mathbf{r}, \qquad \mathbf{v}_2 = \boldsymbol{\omega}_2 \times \mathbf{r}. \tag{7.3}$$

The resultant angular velocity $\boldsymbol{\omega}$ would impart to P the velocity $\mathbf{v}$ given by Equation (7.1). From Equation (7.2) we obtain

$$\boldsymbol{\omega} \times \mathbf{r} = \boldsymbol{\omega}_1 \times \mathbf{r} + \boldsymbol{\omega}_2 \times \mathbf{r}, \tag{7.4}$$

which is also an expression of the parallelogram law. But by Equations (7.1) and (7.2), this equation is just

$$\mathbf{v} = \mathbf{v}_1 + \mathbf{v}_2, \tag{7.5}$$

which tells us that if we represent angular velocities by vectors as above, the instantaneous velocities imparted to P by $\boldsymbol{\omega}_1$ and $\boldsymbol{\omega}_2$ have a vectorial resultant that is just the velocity that would be imparted to P by the vectorial resultant of $\boldsymbol{\omega}_1$ and $\boldsymbol{\omega}_2$. Since this holds for *every* point P of the rigid body, we are justified in treating angular velocities as vectors.

Note in the above how important it is that the position vector $\mathbf{r}$ of P should be the same throughout. We could not have obtained Equation (7.4) from Equation (7.2) otherwise. Therefore, we must here regard the angular velocities $\boldsymbol{\omega}$, $\boldsymbol{\omega}_1$, and $\boldsymbol{\omega}_2$ as having lines of action all passing through a common point O. As here regarded, they are, thus, not free vectors but sliding vectors.

That they are not free vectors is clear from the fact that if we spin a rigid body about an axis we do not cause the same motion as when we spin it with the same angular speed about a parallel axis that does not coincide with the first. Despite this, if we are willing to be content with the changes of orientation produced by angular velocities and to ignore the actual motions of individual points, we can think of angular velocities as free vectors.

Exercise 7.5 Verify the above by considering the motion of a rigid rod AB in a plane if the rod is spun about an axis through A perpendicular to the plane, and if it is spun about a parallel axis through B.

Exercise 7.6 You are probably familiar with *Foucault's pendulum.* It is merely a pendulum suspended in such a way that the support does not influence the direction in which the pendulum swings. What makes this simple piece of apparatus fascinating is that it reveals the rotation of the earth without our needing to look at the stars or other external objects to take our bearings. For example, if the pendulum were mounted at a pole, the vertical plane in which it swings would appear to rotate once every 24 hours. What really happens is that the pendulum swings in a plane that may be described as fixed in direction relative to the so-called fixed stars, and the earth rotates once every 24 hours beneath it. At the equator, the pendulum would not exhibit any such rotation relative to the earth. Why not?

Exercise 7.7 At what rate relative to the earth would a Foucault pendulum seem to rotate if it were at a place of latitude $\lambda°$? [*Hint*: Let O be the center of the earth and P the point of support of the pendulum. Then we can resolve the angular velocity vector of the earth, say $\boldsymbol{\omega}$, into two components through O, one of magnitude $\omega \sin \lambda$ having its axis along OP, the other of magnitude $\omega \cos \lambda$ perpendicular to OP. Only the former will be revealed by the Foucault pendulum. Note how difficult it would be to visualize the situation without the concept of the angular velocity vector.]

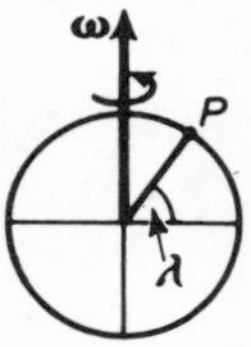

We must now return to the deliberately vague phrase "suppose that the rigid body was somehow subjected to two angular velocities $\boldsymbol{\omega}_1$ and $\boldsymbol{\omega}_2$ simultaneously" [see page 89]. What does it mean? There are two interpretations. Imagine the rigid body mounted on another body that is also rotating. Then if the first has angular velocity $\boldsymbol{\omega}_1$ relative to the second, and the second has angular velocity $\boldsymbol{\omega}_2$ relative to some master reference frame, the first is being subjected simultaneously to the two angular velocities $\boldsymbol{\omega}_1$ and $\boldsymbol{\omega}_2$, and its angular velocity relative to the master frame is the vectorial resultant of $\boldsymbol{\omega}_1$ and $\boldsymbol{\omega}_2$. We are using two reference frames here, just as we did for ordinary velocities when we considered a point moving on a moving platform.

But we can also take the mathematical instead of the physical point of view, just as we did when we looked upon ordinary velocity as the rate of change of displacement with respect to time and could thus combine velocities that were all measured relative to the same reference frame. With angular velocities the situation is as follows. Suppose a rigid body has angular velocity $\boldsymbol{\omega}$ about an axis through O. If we introduce a reference frame $\mathbf{e}_x$, $\mathbf{e}_y$, and $\mathbf{e}_z$ and write:

$$\boldsymbol{\omega}=\omega_x\mathbf{e}_x+\omega_y\mathbf{e}_y+\omega_z\mathbf{e}_z, \tag{7.6}$$

where the components ω_x, ω_y, and ω_z are found in the usual vectorial way, then the instantaneous velocity of each point of the rigid body, as given by

Equation (7.1), will also be correctly given by applying Equation (7.1) to the vectors $\omega_x \mathbf{e}_x$, $\omega_y \mathbf{e}_y$, and $\omega_z \mathbf{e}_z$ to obtain three velocity vectors, and then forming the resultant of these component velocity vectors.

Exercise 7.8 Relative to **i**, **j**, and **k** a rigid body has angular velocity $\boldsymbol{\omega}$ having components $(\omega/\sqrt{2}, \omega/\sqrt{2}, 0)$. A point P on the x-axis has a position vector with components $(r, 0, 0)$. Draw a picture to see what is going on. Then calculate the instantaneous velocity of P (a) by working directly with $\boldsymbol{\omega}$ and forming $\boldsymbol{\omega} \times \mathbf{r}$ and (b) by finding the component velocities $(\omega_x \mathbf{i}) \times \mathbf{r}$ and $(\omega_y \mathbf{j}) \times \mathbf{r}$ and finding their resultant. In which direction does the instantaneous velocity of P point?

Exercise 7.9 Like Exercise 7.8, but with the components of the position vector of P given by $(0, 0, r)$.

Exercise 7.10 Like Exercises 7.8 and 7.9, but with the components of the position vector given by $(r/\sqrt{2}, 0, r/\sqrt{2})$. [Note the sudden increase in complexity here so far as visualization of the motions is concerned. The mathematical manipulations, on the contrary, are almost as easy as before.]

All this time we must have been wondering how it happens that angular velocities behave like vectors despite the fact that angular displacements do not. Here is the essential reason: If we make an angular displacement of a rigid body about a fixed axis, the points of the body move on arcs of circles. Suppose the point P moves on the circle with center N to the position P', as shown in Figure 7.2. Then the displacement PP' is not, in general, perpendicular to the position vector $\overrightarrow{OP}$, nor does it make a fixed angle with $\overrightarrow{OP}$ for all positions of P'—or for all positions of P.

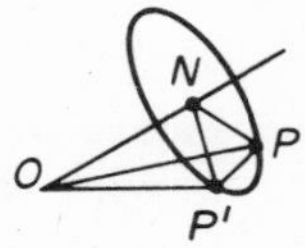

Figure 7.2

Look back at the discussion of the vectorial character of angular velocity and you will see that it depended crucially on the fact that the instantaneous velocity of P was always perpendicular to the position vector of P. We might, if pressed, have managed even if the angle had not been a right angle, provided it had been a fixed angle. But with a varying angle we are beaten.

Even so, how does it happen that the instantaneous velocity of P, which is, after all, just a time rate of change of a displacement, is always perpendicular to P? The reason is that we are dealing with the *instantaneous* velocity. This is, roughly speaking, the time rate of change of an extremely small displacement. If we take PP' extremely small in Figure 7.2 we see that it does indeed make approximately 90° with OP, being approximately tangent to the circle at P. And the fact is that extremely small angular displacements do indeed behave approximately like vectors, so that one often hears it said that infinitesimal angular displacements are vectors even though finite angular displacements are not.

8. MOMENTUM AND ANGULAR MOMENTUM

If a particle of mass m has velocity $\mathbf{v}$, the vector $m\mathbf{v}$ is called its *momentum.* The combination $m\mathbf{v}$ is a rather natural one. Newton regarded it as measuring the quantity of motion. For example, if two particles of mass m are moving with velocity $\mathbf{v}$, there is twice as much motion as with one; and the total momentum adds up to $2m\mathbf{v}$, accurately reflecting the fact.

In collisions momentum is *conserved*; that is, the total momentum vector of the system before the collision is equal to the total momentum vector after the collision.

Exercise 8.1 A particle of mass m moves in the positive direction along the x-axis with speed v. Another particle, of mass $2m$ moves in the positive direction along the y-axis with speed v. The two collide at the origin and coalesce into a single particle. What is the velocity of this particle?

Solution The momenta of the original particles are $mv\mathbf{i}$ and $2mv\mathbf{j}$ respectively. The resulting particle has mass $2m$. So if its velocity is $\mathbf{V}$, its momentum is $2m\mathbf{V}$. But the resultant of the original momenta is $mv\mathbf{i} + 2mv\mathbf{j}$. So, since the momentum is conserved in the collision, we must have $2m\mathbf{V} = mv\mathbf{i} + 2mv\mathbf{j}$; and from this we see that $\mathbf{V} = (v/2)\mathbf{i} + v\mathbf{j}$. Thus, the resulting particle moves with speed $\sqrt{5}\,v/2$ in a direction making an angle $\tan^{-1} 2$ with the positive x-axis.

Exercise 8.2 Like Exercise 8.1 but with a third particle, of mass m, moving with speed $2v$ in the positive direction along the z-axis, all three particles meeting simultaneously at O and coalescing into a single particle. [*Ans.* Speed $3v/4$, and moving in a direction having direction cosines $(\frac{1}{3}, \frac{2}{3}, \frac{2}{3})$. Note that had the resulting particle in Exercise 8.1 later been struck by a particle of mass m moving parallel to the z-axis in the positive direction with speed $2v$, and had this particle coalesced with the one it struck, the resulting speed and direction would be the same as before, though the velocity vector would have a different location.]

Exercise 8.3 A particle of mass m moving with speed v in the $\mathbf{i}$ direction suddenly splits apart into two pieces. One piece, of mass m_1, moves with speed v_1 in the $\mathbf{j}$ direction. How does the other piece move?

[*Ans.* Its velocity is $\dfrac{mv}{m - m_1}\mathbf{i} - \dfrac{m_1 v_1}{m - m_1}\mathbf{j}$.]

Exercise 8.4 Like Exercise 8.3 if the piece having mass m moves with speed v in a direction having direction cosines $\cos\alpha$, $\cos\beta$, and $\cos\gamma$.

The momentum vector is often denoted by the symbol $\mathbf{p}$. If a particle has momentum $\mathbf{p}$ and, relative to a point O, position vector $\mathbf{r}$, the vector product $\mathbf{r} \times \mathbf{p}$ is called the *moment of momentum* of the particle about O. It is often also called the *angular momentum* of the particle about O.

From the basic equation of motion $\mathbf{F} = m\mathbf{a}$, which is valid in an unaccelerated reference frame, we have:

$$\mathbf{r} \times \mathbf{F} = \mathbf{r} \times (m\mathbf{a}). \tag{8.1}$$

It happens that $\mathbf{r} \times (m\mathbf{a})$ is the rate of change of $\mathbf{r} \times (m\mathbf{v})$ with respect to time. This is not obvious, despite the fact that $\mathbf{a}$ is the rate of change of $\mathbf{v}$ with respect to time, since not only $\mathbf{v}$ but also $\mathbf{r}$ changes with time. However it does happen to be true (it can be easily proved using the calculus), so let us accept it as such here. Then Equation (8.1) tells us that the moment about an unaccelerated point O of the force acting on a particle is equal to the rate of change of the angular momentum of the particle about O. In particular, if the force has zero moment about O the angular momentum will be constant, since its rate of change is zero.

Exercise 8.5 A particle acted on by zero force moves in a straight line with uniform speed. Verify that its moment of momentum about a fixed point O is constant.

Exercise 8.6 If a planet is acted on only by the force of gravity directed towards the center of the sun, show that its angular momentum about the center of the sun must be constant, and therefore, that it travels fastest in its orbit at the place where the tangent line to the orbit is closest to the sun.

A *gyroscope* is essentially just a top, though usually one of special shape and mounted in a special way. Consider the gyroscope shown, consisting of a massive squat cylinder spinning on its axis and mounted in such a way that its axis can turn freely in any direction about the center of symmetry O, which is kept in a fixed position. In practice, this requires a moderately elaborate mounting mechanism, but we can here think of the gyroscope as freely pivoted at O. Each particle of the gyroscope has a moment of momentum about O, and the sum of all these moments of momentum is the moment of momentum of the gyroscope about O. Denote it by vector $\mathbf{M}$ lying along the axis.

Equation (8.1) holds for each particle of the gyroscope, and by adding up the equations for all the particles (the mathematicians can do this rigorously) we find that the total moment of the forces acting on the gyroscope is equal to the rate of change of its total angular momentum.

Since the gyroscope is mounted at its center of symmetry, the gravitational forces on it have zero resultant moment about O. Suppose we point the axis of the gyroscope horizontally towards the right as shown in Figure 8.1. Since the resultant moment of the forces acting on it is zero, its angular momentum vector $\mathbf{M}$ will not change. Therefore, it will continue to point in the same direction. Now suppose we exert a constant pressure downward on the tip, P, of the axis, say by hanging a weight on it. How will the axis move? One's first guess—provided one has never played with a gyroscope—is that the tip of the axis will drop vertically. But it will not.

The weight on the tip of the axis exerts on the gyroscope a force whose moment vector about O is in the direction of the horizontal line OQ perpendicular to the axis OP, as shown. It will, therefore, cause the angular momentum vector of the gyroscope to change vectorially at a rate equal to this moment. We can think of the force as continually pumping into the gyroscope angular momentum that always points horizontally at right angles to the position of OP as indicated in the figure by the arrow-headed line segment OQ. By forming the vectorial resultant of $\mathbf{M}$ and a small horizontal additional angular momentum perpendicular to it, we see that the effect of this pumping is to turn the axis of the gyroscope *horizontally* counterclockwise as viewed from above.

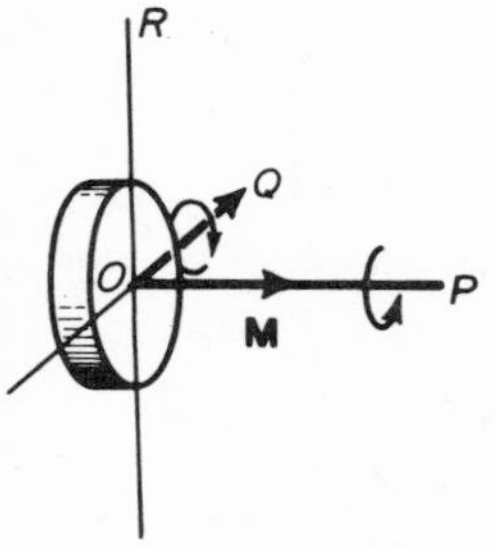

Figure 8.1

Exercise 8.7 In what direction would the turning effect be if, instead of tying a weight to the tip of the axis, we exerted an upward pressure on it?

Exercise 8.8 Like Exercise 8.7 if we pushed the tip of the axis horizontally into the page.

Exercise 8.9 Assume that the propellers of an airplane are all turning in a clockwise sense as viewed from behind. If, in flight, the pilot turns the airplane towards the right, what is the gyroscopic effect of the propellers? [*Ans.* It tends to turn the nose of the airplane downward.]

We have seen that, when a weight is tied to the tip of the axis of the gyroscope in Figure 8.1, the axis will tend to rotate horizontally. When the weight is applied abruptly, the tip of the axis has a tendency to dip as well as to move horizontally and the resulting motion is somewhat complex, the tip of the axis bobbing up and down as the vertical plane containing it sweeps around like a revolving door. However, if the weight is applied gradually and the axis is allowed to find its appropriate motion one can manage, in principle, to end up with the axis turning steadily in a horizontal plane. Since the manifest cause of this horizontal motion of the axis is the *vertical* force exerted by the weight, this is likely to strike us as curious, to say the least. Let us therefore consider what is happening without making use of cross products. For simplicity, regard the gyroscope as a circular disc and consider the motion of a point A on the rim of the gyroscope that is vertically above O, as in Figure 8.2. Because the gyroscope is spinning about its axis, the point A has an instantaneous velocity tangent to the disc that we can represent by the arrow-headed line segment $\overrightarrow{AB}$. When we apply the weight at P we tend to pull OP downward; but this will tend to move the point A *horizontally*, giving it an additional velocity that we can represent by $\overrightarrow{AC}$. The resultant velocity of A, given by $\overrightarrow{AD}$, thus lies outside the plane of the disc and shows that the disc tends to turn about a vertical axis in the manner already discussed. Had we taken a point diametrically opposite to A, both component velocities would be reversed in direction as, therefore, the resultant would be too, thus confirming the turning effect. Had we taken intermediate points the turning effect would be in the same general direction, except for points on the line OQ which would seem to be unaffected. But since the gyroscope is reasonably rigid, even these points must join in the general turning. Indeed, the whole turning is a compromise among discordant local turning effects, and we see that when we tie a weight to the tip of the axis of a spinning gyroscope and thereby cause its axis to rotate in a horizontal plane we introduce considerable internal stresses of a quite complicated sort. But then, even if we did not tie a weight to the tip, the spinning of the gyroscope on its axis would still cause internal stresses, these being sometimes so great as to cause the gyroscope to explode into pieces.

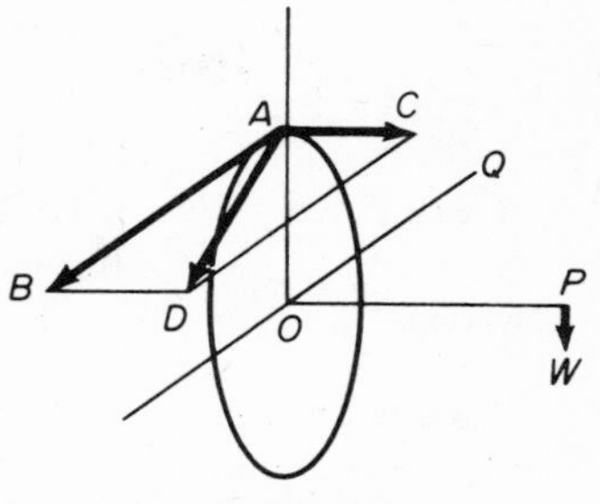

Figure 8.2

9. AREAS AND VECTORIAL ADDITION

When we consider vector products like $\mathbf{r} \times \mathbf{F}$ that yield moments, we have no qualms about accepting the physical fact that they combine according to the parallelogram law. But what about vector products that we think of as representing areas? Having decided that $\mathbf{U} \times \mathbf{V}$ represents the area of a parallelogram both in magnitude and, via the normal to the area, in direction, and having irrevocably agreed that cross products combine vectorially, we must face the fact that actual areas do not seem to fit into the vectorial scheme. For example, in Figure 9.1, if the cross product $\mathbf{U} \times \mathbf{V}$ represents the area of the parallelogram $OLMN$, then $\mathbf{V} \times \mathbf{U}$ represents the area of the parallelogram $ONML$, and we have to count this as the negative of the former area, even though the amount of paint we would need to paint the one is equal to and not the negative of the amount we would need to paint the other. But this is not too far removed from the idea of treating distances along a line as positive in one direction and negative in the opposite direction; and we have learned to live with that and even to approve of it as a valuable mathematical concept. So for the sake of mathematical harmony, and possible benefit, let us accept the official mathematical convention of counting an area as positive if, when "walking" around its rim (we may be somewhat upside down when doing so), we keep the area on our left, and negative if we keep it on our right.

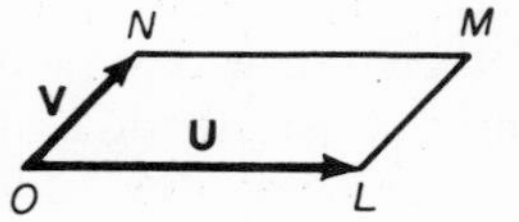

Figure 9.1

Immediately, we find ourselves rewarded by something pretty. For let us place two rectangles $LMNP$ and $MQRN$ side by side as in Figure 9.2 so that the sum of their areas is the area of the rectangle $LQRP$. Then consider the "sum" of the rims of the original rectangles. The part $\overrightarrow{MN}$ of the first can be regarded as cancelling the part $\overrightarrow{NM}$ of the second so that, in a reasonable sense, we can say that the rim of the sum of the areas is equal to the sum of their rims.

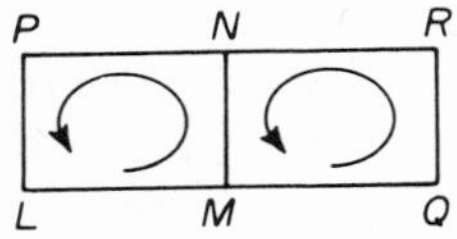

Figure 9.2

Exercise 9.1 Show that it is not necessary for $LMNP$ and $MQRN$ to be rectangles, or even to have straight sides, so long as the areas are contiguous. [Actually they need not be contiguous, but then the prettiness is gone.]

Exercise 9.2 Show that if an irregularly shaped region is crisscrossed by lines, as in Figure 9.3, and the areas of the small regions into which it is divided are all taken positively, then the sum of the rims of these small regions is just the rim of the whole region. Would this be true if all the areas were taken negatively?

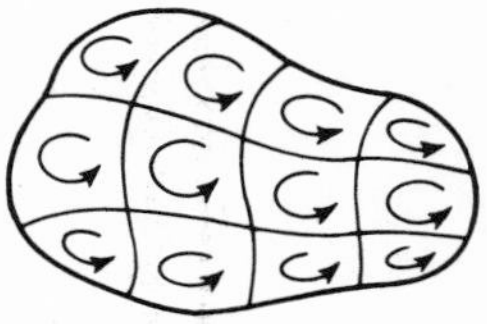

Figure 9.3

Exercise 9.3 Observe that the sum of the areas of $OLMN$ and $ONML$ in Figure 9.1 is zero, and that the sum of their rims is too. Is this true of any two areas, one of which is counted as positive and the other, having the same number of square inches, is counted as negative? [Consider $\mathbf{U} \times \mathbf{V}$ and $(\frac{1}{2}\mathbf{V}) \times (2\mathbf{U})$. Note here, incidentally, that two areas of different shapes can nevertheless cancel each other vectorially.]

Exercise 9.4 In Figure 9.1, if the parallelogram were rotated about O while remaining in the plane, what would be the effect on $\mathbf{U} \times \mathbf{V}$?

Well, we have weathered the first crisis, and even benefited from it. But Exercises 9.3 and 9.4 have reminded us of something else that needs to be explored: the same vector can represent the areas of all sorts of parallelograms—a fact that we have already used, for example, in discussing $\mathbf{A} \times \mathbf{B} + \mathbf{C} \times \mathbf{D}$.

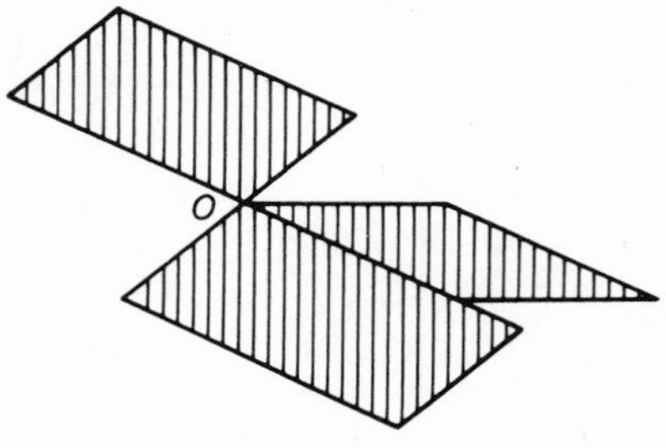

Figure 9.4

Suppose we have three parallelograms in a plane, as in Figure 9.4. Each of them can be represented by a vector through O perpendicular to the plane. The resultant of the three vectors represents the area of the shaded jagged region—which is not a parallelogram.

Indeed, if we are willing to treat the vector representing a plane area as a free vector, we can represent a plane area of quite general shape by means of a vector—simply by breaking the area up into a sufficient number of parallelograms and taking the sum of the corresponding vectors, all of which are parallel to one another. Infinitely many tiny parallelograms may be needed and a proper investigation would involve ideas belonging to the calculus. But the fact is that we can represent by means of a vector a plane area of any shape—even a curved one.

Exercise 9.5 Must the plane area be all in one piece?

Exercise 9.6 A circle of radius 10 ft. lies on the horizontal ground. What are the magnitude and direction of the vector by which a man would represent the circular area if he were walking around it with the area on his right? [*Ans.* Magnitude 100π ft^2., and pointing vertically downward.]

Let us recall that all this began in an innocent attempt to use $UV \sin \theta$ because it had geometrical interest: the area of the parallelogram defined by **U** and **V**. Soon we found ourselves looking on it as a vector, and now we are finding all sorts of unexpected consequences. We are no longer confined to parallelograms, nor even to cross products $\mathbf{U} \times \mathbf{V}$. Willy-nilly, we have had to give vectorial character in their own right to plane areas of all shapes, and this was forced on us by a special case only: the combination of cross products pointing in the same direction. We have still to consider what is forced on us by our combining areas vectorially in the general case.

We start with the relatively simple case of the rectangle $CDEB$ shown in Figure 9.5. Let the area of the rectangle be K. If vector $\overrightarrow{NP}$ represents this area (we have drawn it as a free vector) its magnitude is K and its direction cosines are 0, $\sin \theta$, and $\cos \theta$.

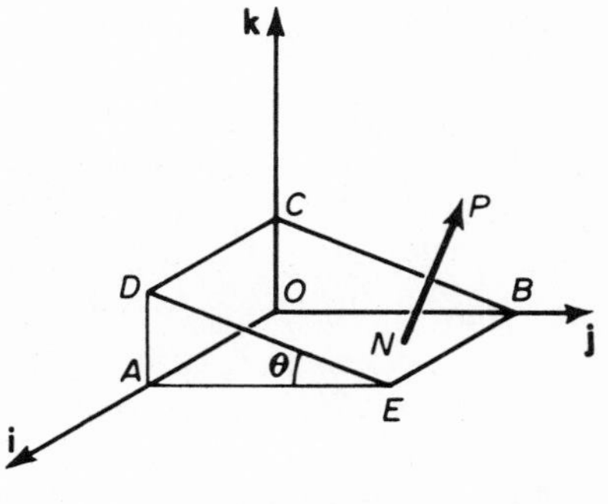

Figure 9.5

Exercise 9.7 Prove that the direction cosines are as stated. [Note that $\overrightarrow{NP}$ is parallel to the **jk**-plane.]

Consequently the components of $\overrightarrow{NP}$ are $(0,\ K \sin \theta,\ K \cos \theta)$. But since the rectangle $OAEB$ is the projection of $CDEB$ on the **ij**-plane its area is $K \cos \theta$; so we see that the **k** component of $\overrightarrow{NP}$ is the area of the projection of $CDEB$ on the **ij**-plane. More, we see that the component *vector* of $\overrightarrow{NP}$ in the **k** direction, namely $(K \cos \theta)\mathbf{k}$, represents both in magnitude and direction the projection of $CDEB$ on the **ij**-plane. Similarly, the component vector of

$\overrightarrow{NP}$ in the **j** direction represents the projection of the original area $CDEB$ on the **ki**-plane.

Exercise 9.8 Prove the last assertion.

Exercise 9.9 Prove that a corresponding assertion is valid for the component vector in the **i** direction and the projection of the area on the **jk**-plane.

We can easily generalize this result to the case of any plane region oriented in any way relative to **i**, **j**, and **k**. The crucial fact that we have to use is that the angle between two planes is the same as the angle between their normals. Let the region have area K and let a line normal to it have direction cosines $\cos\alpha$, $\cos\beta$, and $\cos\gamma$. Then the vector **V** representing the area of the plane region is given by:

$$\mathbf{V} = (K\cos\alpha)\mathbf{i} + (K\cos\beta)\mathbf{j} + (K\cos\gamma)\mathbf{k}. \tag{9.1}$$

Since the normal makes an angle γ with **k** (which is normal to the **ij**-plane), the plane region makes the same angle γ with the **ij**-plane. So its projection on the **ij**-plane has area $K\cos\gamma$, and we see that THE COMPONENT VECTOR IN THE **k** DIRECTION OF THE VECTOR **V**, NAMELY $(K\cos\gamma)\mathbf{k}$, REPRESENTS IN MAGNITUDE AND DIRECTION THE PROJECTION OF THE REGION ON THE **ij**-PLANE. SIMILAR RESULTS HOLD FOR THE OTHER COMPONENT VECTORS.

While this is an important theorem, and a useful one, it is stated in terms of **i**, **j**, and **k**, and it applies, at most, to reference frames in which the base vectors $\mathbf{e}_x$, $\mathbf{e}_y$, and $\mathbf{e}_z$ are mutually orthogonal. (For more general reference frames it can be restated in terms of oblique instead of orthogonal projections, but then it takes on a somewhat different character.) Meanwhile, Equation (9.1) confronts us with a stark fact that we have been trying to avoid: when we treat areas vectorially we commit ourselves to agreeing, for example, that three areas lying respectively in the **jk**-plane, the **ki**-plane, and the **ij**-plane are somehow to be regarded as together equivalent to a single area that lies in none of these planes, and that contains fewer square inches than the three do together.

Our first reaction is that this is preposterous. But we recall that when we said of ordinary vectors that $\overrightarrow{OA} + \overrightarrow{OB} = \overrightarrow{OC}$, the corresponding parallelogram diagram seemed equally preposterous. By a process of abstraction we came, via the idea of shifts, to the idea of displacements, and then at last we could accept the vectorial law of combination geometrically. We have to try to do something of the same sort with areas.

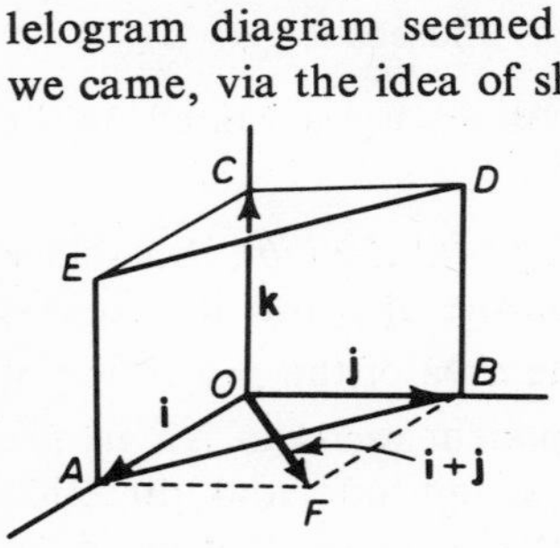

Figure 9.6

Instead of returning to Figure 9.5, let us avoid page-turning by considering a similar but even simpler situation that lends itself better to what we wish to discuss. The cross products $\mathbf{j} \times \mathbf{k}$ and $\mathbf{k} \times \mathbf{i}$ are respectively **i** and **j** and they can represent the areas of the squares $OBDC$ and $OCEA$

in Figure 9.6, though they could also represent differently shaped areas. The resultant of **i** and **j** is $\mathbf{i} + \mathbf{j}$, which is shown as $\overrightarrow{OF}$. This latter vector can represent the area of the rectangle $ABDE$ if we think of it as a free vector.

Exercise 9.10 Show that the magnitude of $\mathbf{i} + \mathbf{j}$ does indeed give the area of $ABDE$, that $\mathbf{i} + \mathbf{j}$ is normal to $ABDE$, and that it points in the direction appropriate to $ABDE$ and not to $AEDB$.

When we say that $\mathbf{j} \times \mathbf{k} + \mathbf{k} \times \mathbf{i} = \mathbf{i} + \mathbf{j}$, we say that, vectorially speaking, the areas of the squares $OBDC$ and $OCEA$ are together somehow equivalent to the area of the rectangle $ABDE$ (though not to that of $AEDB$). We notice that triangles DCE and BOA have the same area. Since they are parallel, we can represent them by equal free vectors. Then if we reverse the sense of one of them, their sum will be zero. So let us add to the two squares $OBDC$ and $OCEA$ the pair of self-cancelling triangles DEC and BOA. [Note the order: DEC, not DCE.] Then, from the vectorial point of view, we have to regard these four patches taken together as equivalent to the area $ABDE$. And what we now notice with the sudden delight that attends discovery, is that *the four patches taken together have the same rim as the area ABDE.*

Exercise 9.11 Prove that the rims are as stated. [Note the various cancellations: for example, the $\overrightarrow{DC}$ of the square $OBDC$ cancels the $\overrightarrow{CD}$ of the triangle DEC.]

Now the question arises: is this just a coincidence or an instance of a general theorem? The matter is worth exploring. Consider a tetrahedron with vertices P, A, B, and C, as shown in Figure 9.7. Working with displacements, we see that $\overrightarrow{BC} = \overrightarrow{PC} - \overrightarrow{PB}$ and $\overrightarrow{CA} = \overrightarrow{PA} - \overrightarrow{PC}$. So, using the fact that $\overrightarrow{PC} \times \overrightarrow{PC} = 0$, we have

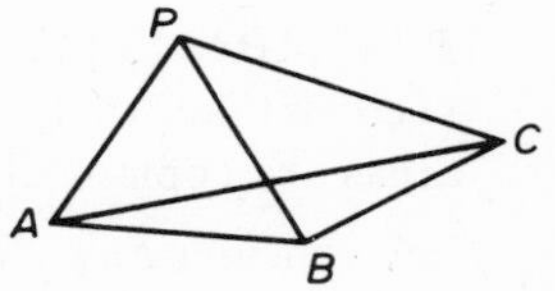

Figure 9.7

$$\tfrac{1}{2}\overrightarrow{BC} \times \overrightarrow{CA} = \tfrac{1}{2}(\overrightarrow{PC} - \overrightarrow{PB}) \times (\overrightarrow{PA} - \overrightarrow{PC}) = \tfrac{1}{2}\overrightarrow{PB} \times \overrightarrow{PC} + \tfrac{1}{2}\overrightarrow{PC} \times \overrightarrow{PA} + \tfrac{1}{2}\overrightarrow{PA} \times \overrightarrow{PB}.$$

[Note the change of sign when we reversed the order of the factors in the term $-\tfrac{1}{2}\overrightarrow{PB} \times \overrightarrow{PA}$.] This relation has an immediate geometrical interpretation. The cross product $\tfrac{1}{2}\overrightarrow{BC} \times \overrightarrow{CA}$ represents vectorially the area of the triangle ABC, the vector pointing upward if we think of ABC as horizontal.

Exercise 9.12 Why upward? [Note that $\overrightarrow{BC} = -\overrightarrow{CB}$.]

Also $\tfrac{1}{2}\overrightarrow{PB} \times \overrightarrow{PC}$ represents vectorially the area of the triangle PBC, the vector pointing in an upwardish direction—out of, not into the tetrahedron. Similarly for $\tfrac{1}{2}\overrightarrow{PC} \times \overrightarrow{PA}$ and $\tfrac{1}{2}\overrightarrow{PA} \times \overrightarrow{PB}$. Therefore the above relation, based on the distributive law, here tells us that we must regard the area ABC as vectorially equivalent to the three areas PBC, PCA, and PAB taken together. And we note that the rim of the former is the same as the rim of the latter three taken together.

Exercise 9.13 Prove that the rims are as stated.

Exercise 9.14 Prove the corresponding theorem for a pyramid *PABCD* with a four-sided base. [Do it in two ways: (a) without cross products, by regarding the pyramid as two contiguous tetrahedra and applying the above theorem, and (b) by means of cross products as above. In method (b) you will, in effect, be considering two tetrahedra, since you will have to regard the area *ABCD* as the sum of two triangles, such as *ABC* and *BCD*.]

Exercise 9.15 By method (a), extend the result in Exercise 9.14 to the case of a pyramid with an n-sided base.

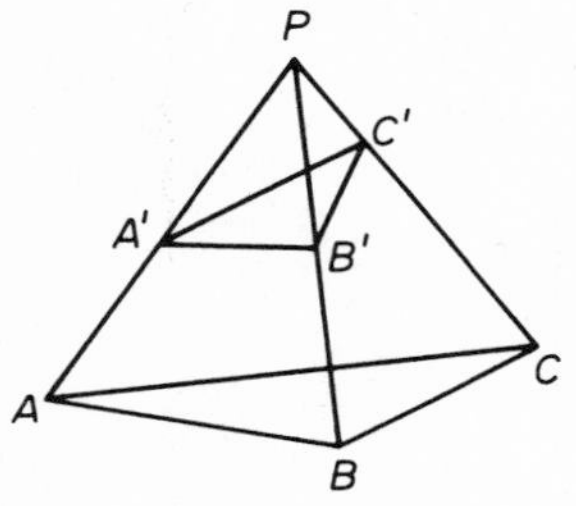

Figure 9.8

Exercise 9.16 In Figure 9.8, the plane $A'B'C'$ is not necessarily parallel to the plane ABC. By "subtracting" the tetrahedron $PA'B'C'$ from the tetrahedron $PABC$, show, without resorting to cross products, that the area ABC is vectorially equivalent to the sum of the areas of $ABB'A'$, $BCC'B'$, $CAA'C'$, and $A'B'C'$, and that the rim of ABC is the rim of the four latter areas taken together. [*Hint*: We have, using a self-explanatory notation, $ABC = PBC + PCA + PAB$, and $A'B'C' = PB'C' + PC'A' + PA'B'$. Subtract, using the vectorial fact that, for example, $PBC - PB'C' = BCC'B'$ because these areas are coplanar.]

Now consider any plane area bounded by a simple closed curve Γ, as in Figure 9.9, and think of it as made of a ductile metal. By means of an appropriately shaped tool and a hammer, beat a tetrahedral dent *PABC* into the surface. Then, vectorially, the area is equivalent to what it was before, because area *ABC* is vectorially equivalent to the three areas *PBC*, *PCA*, and *PAB* taken together.

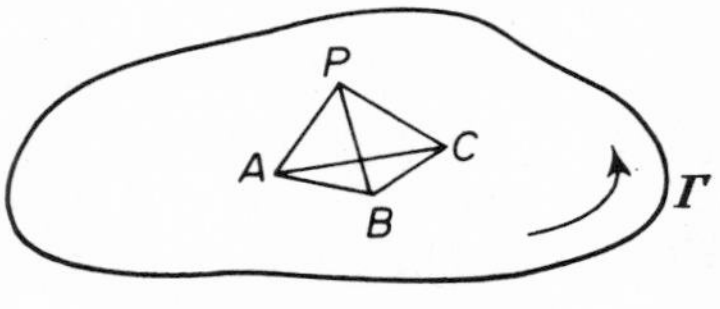

Figure 9.9

What about the rim of the distorted surface? In a sense it is obviously the same as before since the dent, not being a perforation, hardly qualifies as part of the rim. But let us convince ourselves of this. Had we punched out a triangular hole *ABC*, the rim would have been Γ plus the rim of the triangle *taken in the order ACB*—remember, we have to walk the rim with the area on our left. When we add the cap *PABC* we, in effect, add the rim *ABC*, and this just cancels the rim of the punched hole that we had to take in the opposite order.

So we have the important result that by punching the tetrahedral dent we changed neither the vectorial area nor the rim. We now become "punch drunk," making tetrahedral dents all over the place, and we end up with the realization that we can grossly distort the surface without altering its vectorial area, provided we leave its rim undistorted, which means, incidentally, that we may not punch holes in the surface. And we are ready to accept without proof the fact that the result holds even if the original surface is distorted into the shape of a bulging balloon, or a convoluted, semi-inflated one, or worse. The proof involves ideas belonging to the calculus.

At last we seem to understand the situation: areas are to be counted as vectorially equivalent if they have the same boundary. This is not the whole story, however.

Exercise 9.17 Show that *the boundary curve need not be a plane curve.* [Consider, for simplicity, a boundary lying in a plane and in the form of a closed polygon. Now replace one side AB by two lines AP and PB not in the plane. Consider two surfaces having this distorted rim. Add to each the triangle APB and they will now have the same flat rim and, so, will be equivalent. So they must have been equivalent before.]

Exercise 9.18 In Figure 9.6, what is the vector that would represent the area of a surface whose boundary was $OBDCEAO$? [*Ans.* $\mathbf{i} + \mathbf{j}$.]

This is the crux of the matter, but not the whole of it. In our discussion we had to treat areas as *free* vectors. So we must be ready to agree that two areas with congruent, similarly oriented rims are equivalent even if the rims do not coincide. Also we have to remember that, for example, a triangle and a parallelogram of the same area and in parallel planes are represented by the same vector and are thus regarded as equivalent; and that each could be equivalent to an aggregate of several isolated patches of area of suitable size and orientation. Since the exploration of all these possibilities frightens me, I shall pretend I have said enough about them.

There is a remarkable parallelism between the vectorial concept of area and the idea of a displacement. A displacement $\overrightarrow{AB}$ is equivalent to any sequence of zigzag displacements starting at A and ending at B (or, indeed, starting at C and ending at D if $\overrightarrow{CD} = \overrightarrow{AB}$; but for simplicity let us stick to the points A and B here). The points A and B can be regarded as the rim or boundary of the displacement $\overrightarrow{AB}$. So when we wish to treat line segments vectorially we have to agree that all zigzag line segments—or indeed any curved segments—having the same boundary are to be counted as equivalent. Analogously, when we wish to treat surface areas vectorially, we have to agree that, no matter how greatly convoluted they may be, all surfaces having the same boundary are to be counted as equivalent. [But see below.] When we stay with the same end points A and B rather than allowing also equivalent pairs of end points, like C and D, we are dealing with shifts rather than vectors. When we correspondingly keep to areas having the same rim we are dealing with an areal analogue of shifts. In a restricted case, this "*areal shift*" has a simple pictorial significance. Consider a closed curve Γ that is not necessarily plane. Imagine it capped by a suitably bent iron plate, and consider how we would go about protecting *one side* of the plate from rusting because of exposure to rain. We could attach a tarpaulin to the rim Γ in a watertight way, and no matter how large we made the tarpaulin or how we arranged its billows and folds, it would protect the specified side of the iron from the rain. If we wished to protect the other side of the plate instead, we would attach the tarpaulin differently, though to the same rim. How can we specify the side we wish to protect? In conformity with what has gone before, we can associate with each side a sense of walking around the rim. If we walk with the immediate area of the iron cap on our left, we will agree to protect the side on which our feet tread; if on our right, the other side.

> **Exercise 9.19** Show that the above is consistent in that, if we walk around Γ in the opposite sense, the criterion will yield the opposite side in either case.

From all tarpaulin surfaces that protect a given side of the iron plate, we abstract everything except their common rim Γ and the sense in which we go around Γ. The resulting abstraction is the areal shift, and all these surfaces yield the same areal shift.

The difficulty with this picture is that the surfaces we have been likening to tarpaulins can cross the cap. To save the analogy we could make the cap bulge so that none of the protecting surfaces crosses it. But since we have to contemplate all surfaces having the given rim, the bulge would have to be infinitely great. Now that the idea of protection from rusting has served its pictorial purpose for us, we might as well abandon the idea of an iron cap and say that the areal shift is basically the common rim of all the surfaces, but with a particular sense of going around it. Thus it is A RIM AND A SENSE; but with it goes a faint reminiscence of the idea of a covering area, just as an ordinary shift is a pair of points and a sense, but with a faint reminiscence of journeying.

When we go from areal shifts to areal vectors we encounter the frightening pictorial complications already mentioned. But these are analogous to those that arise in the transition from ordinary shifts to displacements, which require us to agree that

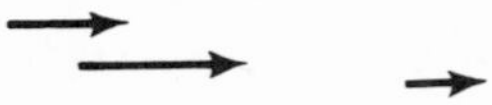

are together equivalent to

and if the situation here is less complex than it is for areas, it is nonetheless analogous to the areal situation.

It is interesting to speculate on the likelihood of our coming to the idea of a vector product had we started out with this concept of areal shifts.

Exercise 9.20 In Figure 9.7, show that if one adopts the convention of representing the areas by normals that point outward from the tetrahedron, the vectorial sum of the four faces is zero. Show also that with this convention the total rim of the four faces together is zero.

Exercise 9.21 Show that VECTORIALLY THE AREA OF A CLOSED POLYHEDRAL SURFACE IS ZERO IF THE VECTORS ALL POINT OUTWARD FROM THE REGION ENCLOSED BY THE FACES. [A simple method is to slice the region into two parts by means of a plane. Then the surface area of each half is equivalent vectorially to the plane area of the polygon of intersection, but the two halves are equivalent to this plane area with opposite signs.]

10. VECTOR PRODUCTS IN RIGHT- AND LEFT-HANDED REFERENCE FRAMES

We have been hinting for some time that there was something yet to be told about the direction of the vector product of two vectors. Suppose we say, as we have been saying all along, that the vector product **A** × **B** points in the direction such that **A**, **B**, and **A** × **B**, in that order, form a right-handed system. Let us take a right-handed reference frame—for simplicity, a unit orthogonal triad, **i**, **j**, **k**—and consider the components relative to it of **A**, **B**, and **C** where

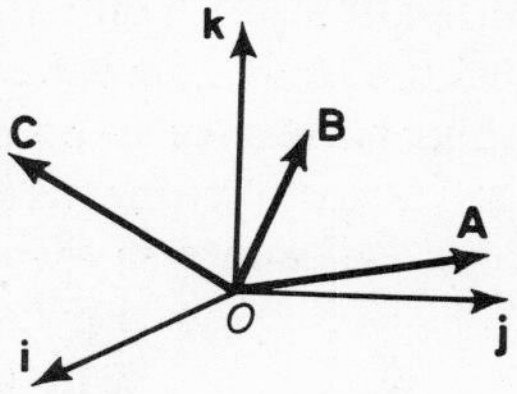

Figure 10.1

$$\mathbf{C} = \mathbf{A} \times \mathbf{B}. \tag{10.1}$$

If **A** and **B** have components (A_x, A_y, A_z) and (B_x, B_y, B_z) respectively, we have seen that **C** has the components $(A_yB_z - A_zB_y, A_zB_x - A_xB_z, A_xB_y - A_yB_x)$.

Now suppose that we reflect Figure 10.1 in a mirror, so that it looks like Figure 10.2—except for the fact that Figure 10.2 has, for example, **B** instead of **ᗺ**. Clearly, the components of the **A** and **B** in Figure 10.2 with respect to **i**, **j**, and **k** in Figure 10.2 will still be (A_x, A_y, A_z) and (B_x, B_y, B_z) respectively. We would therefore like the components of their cross product **C** relative to this **i**, **j**, and **k** frame to be the same as before. But they obviously will not be, because the vector we have labelled **C** in Figure 10.2 is not really **A** × **B** if we adhere to the requirement that **A**, **B**, and **A** × **B**, in that order, shall form a right-handed system. The reflection in the mirror has turned **A**, **B**, and **C** into a left-handed system, and if we adhered to our right-handed convention for the direction of the cross product, we should say that the true **A** × **B** in Figure 10.2 points in the direction opposite to that of the vector labelled **C** in that figure.

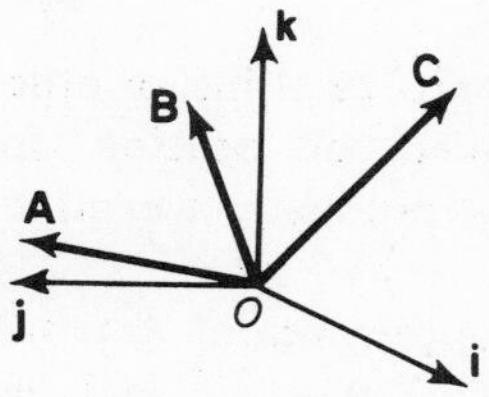

Figure 10.2

We can confirm the existence of the dilemma by forming the cross product $(A_x\mathbf{i} + A_y\mathbf{j} + A_z\mathbf{k}) \times (B_x\mathbf{i} + B_y\mathbf{j} + B_z\mathbf{k})$. At first we imagine we get the same components as before. But that is because we are using the relations $\mathbf{i} \times \mathbf{j} = \mathbf{k}$, etc. Those relations do not hold here, though, if, in calculating $\mathbf{i} \times \mathbf{j}$ etc. we use the convention that **A**, **B**, and **A** × **B** form a right-handed system. Instead of these relations between the **i**, **j**, and **k** in Figure 10.2, we should, by this convention, use $\mathbf{i} \times \mathbf{j} = -\mathbf{k}$, etc; and when we do this we find that the components come out to be the negatives of what they were before.

Now this is very strange behavior for a vector: that when *both it and its reference frame* are reflected in a mirror its components change sign. The vectors **A** and **B** did not behave in this unseemly way.

To preserve some semblance of order we appear to be driven to say that **A** × **B** is a vector perpendicular to **A** and **B** and pointing in a direction that makes **A**, **B**, and **A** × **B** a right-handed system when we are working in terms of a right-handed reference frame, but that it points in a direction that makes **A**, **B**, and **A** × **B** a left-handed system when we are working in terms of a left-handed reference frame. At least, under this convention, if **A** has the same components relative to both frames and **B** has the same components relative to both reference frames, then **A** × **B** will also. But is it wholly satisfactory? It means that if we draw **A** and **B** flat on the page as in Figure 10.3, we cannot say whether **A** × **B**, which is perpendicular to **A** and **B**, points upward toward us or downward away from us until we decide whether, on future occasions, we shall use right-handed reference frames or left-handed ones. And if we simultaneously consult two bystanders, one of whom prefers right-handed frames, and the other left-handed frames we shall be in a grave quandary as to the direction of **A** × **B** in Figure 10.3. Equation (10.1), if true in a right-handed frame, would be false in a left-handed one, unless we said that though **C** was ↗ in a right-handed frame it had to switch to ↙ in a left-handed one, and this would hardly be the sort of vectorial behavior we have hitherto regarded as proper.

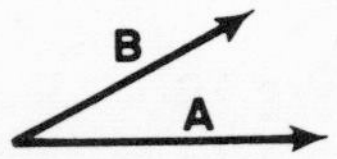

Figure 10.3

11. LOCATION AND CROSS PRODUCTS

Now that our suspicions have been aroused, we begin to think of other curious things about cross products. There is the problem of location, for instance, and while this problem is not confined to cross products, we might as well bring it in here while we are on the warpath.

When we began by thinking of **A** × **B** as representing the area of a parallelogram we had **A** and **B** starting at a common point O. But in the end, we found ourselves regarding the vectors representing areas as free vectors despite the frightening pictorial consequences. Contrast this with the situation in which we deal with moments. Physically, the moment $\mathbf{r} \times \mathbf{F}$ of a force $\mathbf{F}$ about a point O would seem to have to be a vector passing through O. Yet if cross products are free vectors, the moment should presumably be a free vector. In contemplating $\mathbf{A} \times \mathbf{B}$ as an area, we could at least think of $\mathbf{A}$ and $\mathbf{B}$ as displacements, and thus as free vectors, thereby consoling ourselves for having to take $\mathbf{A} \times \mathbf{B}$ as a free vector. But with moments, the situation is different, because $\mathbf{r}$ and $\mathbf{F}$ are not free vectors. Indeed, they do not start from a common point—except in the case of zero moment. If we overlook this and still form $\mathbf{r} \times \mathbf{F}$, which is what we have been doing up to now, we can not assign a reasonable location to $\mathbf{r} \times \mathbf{F}$ because the point P, which is the only reasonable candidate as a localizing point, is *any* point on the line of action of $\mathbf{F}$. If we wish to use O, we may be tempted to add two cancelling forces at O, thus replacing $\mathbf{F}$ by a parallel force $\mathbf{F}_1$, of equal magnitude passing through O, and a couple of moment $\mathbf{r} \times \mathbf{F}$. Then we can form $\mathbf{r} \times \mathbf{F}_1$ and reasonably insist that *its* line of action pass through O. But what shall we then do with the extra, and seemingly superfluous couple? There does not seem to be a satisfactory way out of the dilemma. We would be much better off not talking about it.

Exercise 11.1 Consider the problem of location for the relation $\mathbf{v} = \boldsymbol{\omega} \times \mathbf{r}$.

12. DOUBLE CROSS

Are cross products really vectors? By now we may be beginning to wonder. They have magnitude and direction, they combine according to the parallelogram law, and they obey all the other addenda to the definition that we have thought of so far. Yet they behave queerly in relation to right-handed reference frames. Perhaps we need to add another amendment to the definition. Let us not try to do so, though. Making good definitions is far too difficult. Instead, let us use our general feeling for what is appropriate and what is not, without seeking to formulate sharp criteria.

OUR SUSPICIONS SHOULD HAVE BEEN AROUSED LONG AGO BY THE SEEMINGLY INNOCENT RELATIONS $\mathbf{i} \times \mathbf{j} = \mathbf{k}$, ETC. There is something obviously wrong with them. If the magnitudes of $\mathbf{i}$, $\mathbf{j}$, and $\mathbf{k}$ are lengths measured in, say, feet, then $\mathbf{i} \times \mathbf{j}$ has a magnitude of one square foot and so cannot be the same sort of thing as $\mathbf{k}$, whose magnitude is one foot. Perhaps we counter by arguing that since $\mathbf{i}$, $\mathbf{j}$, and $\mathbf{k}$ are of *unit* length, the magnitudes of $\mathbf{i} \times \mathbf{j}$ and $\mathbf{k}$ have the same numerical value, namely 1. But this will not do. If we change to inches, the former becomes 144 square inches and the latter 12 inches. Clearly, $\mathbf{i} \times \mathbf{j}$ cannot really be $\mathbf{k}$, even though we have been able to get extremely important equations by assuming it is. [Look back at Exercise 9.6 in this connection.]

Again, suppose we consider cross products in two dimensions instead of in three. Then, given two vectors $\mathbf{U}$ and $\mathbf{V}$, we say that their cross product has magnitude $UV \sin \theta$ and that it points—where? Why, nowhere. There is no third dimension into which it can point when we have only two dimensions in all. Clearly the cross product is not a vector in two dimensions.

What about four dimensions? Here again we start by forming the parallelogram defined by two vectors **U** and **V** starting at O. But when we seek a line through O perpendicular to both **U** and **V**, instead of finding no possible directions as in the two-dimensional case, we now find far too many—infinitely many, in fact, and all of them on an equal footing. For in four dimensions, the lines through O perpendicular to both **U** and **V** in general fan out into a plane. So here too the cross product is not a vector. And our conclusion is that in the three-dimensional case too, the cross product is not really a vector, even though by some sort of good fortune it has many of the characteristics of a vector and can be handled much as regular vectors are handled, provided it is handled with care.

Since the cross product in three dimensions has so many of the characteristics of a vector, a good name for an entity of this sort would be *pseudovector*, and this is a particulary apt choice since it happens to be the official technical term for it. [Such entities are sometimes referred to as *axial vectors*.]

13. DIVISION OF VECTORS

The discussion in this section is confined to the three-dimensional case.

Having explored the multiplication of vectors, we naturally wonder how to divide one vector by another. But here too we have to realize that there is no reason why such division should be possible. We have to see if we can find a useful meaning for the quotient of two vectors, and if we cannot, we shall probably wish to keep mum about the matter. There is, of course, no guarantee that the quotient, if it exists, will be a vector: let us recall that we found two reasonable types of "products" of vectors, one yielding scalars and the other pseudovectors. We must therefore be prepared for almost anything here.

Let **U** and **V** be two vectors starting at a common point O. Denote their quotient, if it exists and whatever it may be, by Q, so that we may write:

$$\frac{\mathbf{V}}{\mathbf{U}} = Q. \tag{13.1}$$

Then, since we want to keep as close as possible to our usual ideas of what constitutes the operation of division, we ask that Equation (13.1) mean that

$$\mathbf{V} = Q\mathbf{U}. \tag{13.2}$$

So the quantity Q is to be something that acts on the vector **U** so as to convert it into the vector **V**.

If **U** and **V** have the same line of action, Q is obviously just the ratio of their magnitudes. But we have to consider the case in which they have different directions. To convert **U** to **V** we have to change its magnitude by a factor V/U and also to rotate it so that its direction coincides with that of

V. We find, therefore, that Q involves a ratio of magnitudes and an angular displacement about an axis through O perpendicular to **U** and **V**. Since the specification of the latter requires three numbers, we see that Q requires four. It was therefore called a *quaternion* by W. R. Hamilton, who originated the concept.

This book is not the place to develop the quaternion calculus in any detail, but an extremely sketchy indication of the general idea as it was developed by Hamilton will not be without interest. In what follows, we make various reasonable assertions that, in a fuller treatment, would be listed as axioms.

If triangles OAB and OLM are coplanar, and similar in such a way that OB/OA equals OM/OL rather than OL/OM, then the operation that converts $\overrightarrow{OA}$ into $\overrightarrow{OB}$ is the same as that that converts $\overrightarrow{OL}$ into $\overrightarrow{OM}$. So the quaternions $\overrightarrow{OB}/\overrightarrow{OA}$ and $\overrightarrow{OM}/\overrightarrow{OL}$ are equal. Thus, given a quaternion, we can express it in a form that has as denominator any vector we wish in the plane of the two vectors involved. This being so, we can add two quaternions by first putting them on a common denominator, this latter being a vector lying in the line of intersection of their planes. We then have something of the form $(\overrightarrow{OB}/\overrightarrow{OA}) + (\overrightarrow{OC}/\overrightarrow{OA})$; and since $\overrightarrow{OB}$ and $\overrightarrow{OC}$ are vectors, these quaternions combine by the parallelogram law to yield $\overrightarrow{OR}/\overrightarrow{OA}$, where $\overrightarrow{OR}$ is the resultant of $\overrightarrow{OB}$ and $\overrightarrow{OC}$.

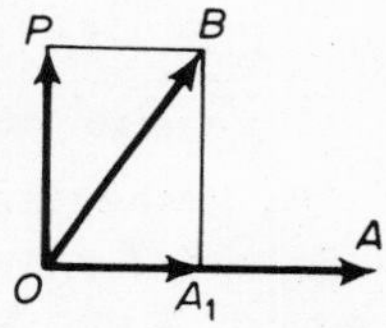

Figure 13.1

We now reverse the idea. Given a quaternion $\overrightarrow{OB}/\overrightarrow{OA}$, we split $\overrightarrow{OB}$ up into two components: $\overrightarrow{OA_1}$ lying along $\overrightarrow{OA}$, and $\overrightarrow{OP}$ perpendicular to it, as in Figure 13.1. Then,

$$\frac{\overrightarrow{OB}}{\overrightarrow{OA}} = \frac{\overrightarrow{OA_1}}{\overrightarrow{OA}} + \frac{\overrightarrow{OP}}{\overrightarrow{OA}}. \tag{13.3}$$

The quantity $\overrightarrow{OA_1}/\overrightarrow{OA}$ was called by Hamilton the *scalar* of the quaternion $\overrightarrow{OB}/\overrightarrow{OA}$. Note that, in general, it is not the same as the ratio of the magnitudes of the vectors $\overrightarrow{OB}$ and $\overrightarrow{OA}$. It is, in fact, their scalar product divided by the square of the magnitude of $\overrightarrow{OA}$. [Hamilton called the ratio of the magnitudes the *tensor*, a word that is now used in a quite different sense, as will be seen in the next chapter.]

Exercise 13.1 Prove the above assertion about the scalar product.

Exercise 13.2 Prove that the scalar of $\overrightarrow{OB}/\overrightarrow{OA}$ plus the scalar of $\overrightarrow{OC}/\overrightarrow{OA}$ is equal to the scalar of $\overrightarrow{OR}/\overrightarrow{OA}$, where $\overrightarrow{OR}$ is the resultant of $\overrightarrow{OB}$ and $\overrightarrow{OC}$.

The quaternion $\overrightarrow{OP}/\overrightarrow{OA}$ in Equation (13.3) is of a special type since it involves a rotation through a right angle. Such quaternions are called *right quaternions*. They turn out to be of special importance.

Hamilton introduced three basic right-quaternions which he denoted by i,

j, and k. These are *not* the same as the vectors **i**, **j**, and **k**, though they have distant kinship with them. They are defined in terms of three mutually perpendicular vectors **X**, **Y**, and **Z**, starting at O, having unit magnitudes, and forming a right-handed system. The right quaternion **Z**/**Y** converts **Y** into **Z**. It is denoted by i, and it involves a rotation through 90° about **X**. From a diagram, one easily sees that i also converts **Z** into $-$**Y**. So we may write:

$$i = \frac{\mathbf{Z}}{\mathbf{Y}} = \frac{-\mathbf{Y}}{\mathbf{Z}}.$$

Similarly, j and k are defined by:

$$j = \frac{\mathbf{X}}{\mathbf{Z}} = \frac{-\mathbf{Z}}{\mathbf{X}}, \qquad k = \frac{\mathbf{Y}}{\mathbf{X}} = \frac{-\mathbf{X}}{\mathbf{Y}}.$$

Exercise 13.3 Show that the scalars of i, j, and k are zero.

By i^2 we mean the result of applying i twice. Since i converts **Y** into **Z**, and the second i converts **Z** into $-$**Y**, i^2 converts **Y** into $-$**Y** and we therefore write $i^2 = -1$.

Exercise 13.4 Prove, similarly, that $j^2 = -1$ and $k^2 = -1$.

By ij we mean the result of applying j and then i. Since j converts **X** into $-$**Z**, and i converts **Z** into $-$**Y** (and thus, as is easily seen, $-$**Z** into **Y**), ij converts **X** into **Y**, which is just what k does. So we write $ij = k$. However, since i converts **Y** into **Z**, and j converts **Z** into **X**, ji converts **Y** into **X**. But k converts **Y** into $-$**X**. Therefore we write $ji = -k$.

Exercise 13.5 Prove, similarly, that $jk = i$, $kj = -i$, $ki = j$, and $ik = -j$.

Exercise 13.6 Prove that $ijk = -1$; also, that $i(ij) = (ii)j = -j$, $i(ji) = (ij)i = j$, and $i(jj) = (ij)j = -i$. [Results such as these show that i, j, and k obey the associative law of multiplication, even though they do not obey the commutative law.]

Consider now a right quaternion, such as $\overrightarrow{OP}/\overrightarrow{OA}$ in Equation (13.3). We can associate with it an entity called its *index*. This consists of an arrow-headed line segment $\overrightarrow{OP'}$ that lies, in the right-handed sense, along the axis of the rotation performed by the quaternion $\overrightarrow{OP}/\overrightarrow{OA}$, and it has a length representing the number OP/OA. Its direction is thus perpendicular to the plane of of $\overrightarrow{OP}$ and $\overrightarrow{OA}$. Since all right quaternions involve rotations through the same angle, 90°, their indices combine according to the parallelogram law.

Exercise 13.7 Prove this. [If $\overrightarrow{OB} + \overrightarrow{OC} = \overrightarrow{OR}$, then $\overrightarrow{OB}/\overrightarrow{OA} + \overrightarrow{OC}/\overrightarrow{OA} = \overrightarrow{OR}/\overrightarrow{OA}$. We obtain the indices of these three quaternions by multiplying $\overrightarrow{OB}$, $\overrightarrow{OC}$, and $\overrightarrow{OR}$ by the same quantity, $1/OA$, and rotating them in their plane through 90° about an axis through O perpendicular to their plane. Compare the analogous discussion in connection with cross products of perpendicular vectors.]

Exercise 13.8 Show that the index of i is the vector **X**.

Thus, provided we stay with right-handed systems, the indices behave like vectors. (They are actually pseudovectors.) So we can express the index $\overrightarrow{OP}'$ of the quaternion $\overrightarrow{OP}/\overrightarrow{OA}$ in the form,

$$\overrightarrow{OP}' = x\mathbf{X} + y\mathbf{Y} + z\mathbf{Z}, \tag{13.4}$$

where (x, y, z) are the coordinates of P' relative to the base vectors **X**, **Y**, and **Z**. Since the indices **X**, **Y**, and **Z** belong respectively to the quaternions i, j, and k, we have, corresponding to Equation (13.4), the quaternion equation:

$$\frac{\overrightarrow{OP}}{\overrightarrow{OA}} = xi + yj + zk, \tag{13.5}$$

and, therefore, such quaternion quantities obey the same algebraic rules as their vectorial indices. If we denote the scalar of the quaternion $\overrightarrow{OB}/\overrightarrow{OA}$ in Equation (13.3), namely $\overrightarrow{OA_1}/\overrightarrow{OA}$, by w, we see from Equation (13.5) that this quaternion, which is any quaternion Q, can be expressed in the form:

$$Q = w + xi + yj + zk. \tag{13.6}$$

The significant thing about this is that the quantities on the right, and thus quaternions in general, obey all the usual rules of algebra except the commutative law of multiplication. Quaternions are thus of considerable theoretical importance quite apart from their relationship to vectors. They constitute what algebraists call a noncommutative *field* (not to be confused with what physicists call a field—when they are talking physics or agricuture rather than algebra). Thus quaternions, like complex numbers, are a natural extension of the idea of number, and are often called *hypercomplex numbers*.

It is worthwhile contemplating Hamilton's achievement. You and I, if the idea had ever occurred to us of discussing the quotient of two vectors, would have noted, perhaps, that it involved the ratio of their magnitudes and also something akin to an angular displacement. The former we would have thought of as a scalar of no particular charm, and the latter would have scared us away from pursuing the idea further. Hamilton, by defining a new scalar, and focusing on *right* quaternions and relatating them to their indices, not only created the essentials of scalar and vector products, but also constructed an algebra of extreme elegance.

Scalar and vector products were conceived by Hamilton and H. Grassmann independently in the 1840's. Since Hamilton's quaternion calculus proved unwieldy for applications to the physics of the nineteenth century, J. W. Gibbs and, independently, O. Heaviside, extracted from it the much more convenient vector calculus that we have been studying in this book. They did so in a creative way, and in the face of bitter opposition from the supporters of quaternionic methods.

When we tried to regard angular displacements as vectors, we were shocked and thwarted by their properties of noncommutativity and worse. We may well wonder, then, that these properties do not destroy Hamilton's structure. One reason is that, for example, the quaternions i, j, and k are not angular displacements but merely relations between pairs of vectors; and another is that Hamilton made the noncommutativity apply to multiplication rather than addition. Even so he was, for a long time, frustrated by the lack of commutativity of angular displacements, and it came to him as a staggering discovery that the key to progress lay in the heretical renunciation of the commutative law of multiplication. When, finally, the idea did come to him he realized immediately that it was a momentous one. But he could not know that almost a century later noncommutative multiplication would prove to be of crucial importance in the quantum theory, and that the spin of atomic particles would actually be represented by symbols satisfying equations corresponding to:

$$ij + ji = 0,$$

as would other fundamental quantities of atomic physics.

Exercise 13.9 Imagine unit vectors **X**, **Y**, and **Z** along the respective coordinate axes in Figures 6.2 and 6.3. Show that the vector **X** in Figure 6.3c occupies the position of **Y** in Figure 6.3a. Denote this by $\mathbf{X} \to \mathbf{Y}$. Show similarly that $\mathbf{Y} \to \mathbf{Z}$, and $\mathbf{Z} \to \mathbf{X}$. Show that the corresponding results for Figure 6.2 are $\mathbf{X} \to -\mathbf{Z}$, $\mathbf{Y} \to \mathbf{X}$, and $\mathbf{Z} \to -\mathbf{Y}$. Note that $\mathbf{X} \to \mathbf{Y}$ is the effect of the quaternion k, while $\mathbf{Y} \to \mathbf{X}$ is that of $-k$, these results being in conformity with $ij = -ji = k$; but note that $\mathbf{X} = -\mathbf{Z}$ is not the effect of k but of j. Consider the other effects similarly. [This exercise indicates the subtlety and boldness of Hamilton's concept: though i, j, and k are *related* to angular displacements, ij does not yield an angular displacement about the z-axis. Despite this, Hamilton, with profound mathematical instinct, did not shy away from quaternion relations $ij = k$ and the like, as you and I would have. He later found a way to represent general angular displacements by means of quaternions.]

6

TENSORS

1. HOW COMPONENTS OF VECTORS TRANSFORM

The time has come for a new approach. To make further progress with vectors, we concentrate on their components. This may seem an unpromising tactic, since the components change whenever we change the reference frame, whereas relations among vectors are independent of the choice of the frame. But by studying how such changeable things as components can embody this objectivity of vectors, we come to an important generalization: the concept of a *tensor*.

We do not propose to discuss location. For this and other reasons we use a fixed origin O and assume that all vectors and the like start at O. To get the feel of how components of vectors behave, we start with a simple numerical example in two dimensions. Suppose we are given

$$\mathbf{V} = V_x \mathbf{e}_x + V_y \mathbf{e}_y, \tag{1.1}$$

and we change to a new reference frame with base vectors $\bar{\mathbf{e}}_x$ and $\bar{\mathbf{e}}_y$ where

$$\left.\begin{aligned} \bar{\mathbf{e}}_x &= 3\mathbf{e}_x + 4\mathbf{e}_y \\ \bar{\mathbf{e}}_y &= \mathbf{e}_x + 2\mathbf{e}_y. \end{aligned}\right\} \tag{1.2}$$

To find how the components change, we first solve Equations (1.2) for $\mathbf{e}_x$ and $\mathbf{e}_y$ in terms of $\bar{\mathbf{e}}_x$ and $\bar{\mathbf{e}}_y$; the result is:

$$\left.\begin{aligned}\mathbf{e}_x &= \bar{\mathbf{e}}_x - 2\bar{\mathbf{e}}_y\\ \mathbf{e}_y &= -\tfrac{1}{2}\bar{\mathbf{e}}_x + \tfrac{3}{2}\bar{\mathbf{e}}_y.\end{aligned}\right\} \tag{1.3}$$

Then from Equations (1.1) and (1.3) we have:

$$\begin{aligned}\mathbf{V} &= V_x(\bar{\mathbf{e}}_x - 2\bar{\mathbf{e}}_y) + V_y(-\tfrac{1}{2}\bar{\mathbf{e}}_x + \tfrac{3}{2}\bar{\mathbf{e}}_y)\\ &= (V_x - \tfrac{1}{2}V_y)\bar{\mathbf{e}}_x + (-2V_x + \tfrac{3}{2}V_y)\bar{\mathbf{e}}_y.\end{aligned} \tag{1.4}$$

But the components $\bar{V}_x$ and $\bar{V}_y$ in the new reference frame must satisfy an equation corresponding to Equation (1.1), namely,

$$\mathbf{V} = \bar{V}_x\bar{\mathbf{e}}_x + \bar{V}_y\bar{\mathbf{e}}_y. \tag{1.5}$$

So Equation (1.4) shows that the new components of $\mathbf{V}$ are given by

$$\left.\begin{aligned}\bar{V}_x &= V_x - \tfrac{1}{2}V_y\\ \bar{V}_y &= -2V_x + \tfrac{3}{2}V_y.\end{aligned}\right\} \tag{1.6}$$

Compare the coefficients in Equations (1.6) and (1.3).

Exercise 1.1 If $\mathbf{V} = V_x\mathbf{e}_x + V_y\mathbf{e}_y$, find its components relative to $\bar{\mathbf{e}}_x$ and $\bar{\mathbf{e}}_y$, where $\bar{\mathbf{e}}_x = 4\mathbf{e}_x + \mathbf{e}_y$ and $\bar{\mathbf{e}}_y = 2\mathbf{e}_x + \mathbf{e}_y$. [*Ans.* From $\mathbf{e}_x = \frac{1}{2}\bar{\mathbf{e}}_x - \frac{1}{2}\bar{\mathbf{e}}_y$ and $\mathbf{e}_y = -\bar{\mathbf{e}}_x + 2\bar{\mathbf{e}}_y$, we obtain $\bar{V}_x = \frac{1}{2}V_x - V_y$ and $\bar{V}_y = -\frac{1}{2}V_x + 2V_y$. Explain why the coefficients of the V's automatically come out to be the same as those of the e's, though in different places.]

Exercise 1.2 Like Exercise 1.1 for $\bar{\mathbf{e}}_x = \mathbf{e}_x - 2\mathbf{e}_y$ and $\bar{\mathbf{e}}_y = -\frac{1}{2}\mathbf{e}_x + \frac{3}{2}\mathbf{e}_y$, and compare with the example worked out in the text.

2. THE INDEX NOTATION

In three dimensions, we have been denoting the base vectors by $\mathbf{e}_x$, $\mathbf{e}_y$, and $\mathbf{e}_z$, and the components of a vector by V_x, V_y, and V_z. In four dimensions we already find ourselves in a squeeze when we try to think of what letter to add to x, y, and z, and in n dimensions, especially when $n > 26$, the inconvenience of using different letters becomes considerable. So we use numbers instead, denoting the base vectors, for example, by $\mathbf{e}_1, \mathbf{e}_2, \ldots, \mathbf{e}_n$. Then we denote all these e's collectively by the single symbol $\mathbf{e}_a$, where a takes on the values $1, 2, \ldots, n$, in turn. Thus, in three dimensions, a takes on the values 1, 2, and 3, and $\mathbf{e}_a$ stands for $\mathbf{e}_1$, $\mathbf{e}_2$, and $\mathbf{e}_3$, which are our new symbols for $\mathbf{e}_x$, $\mathbf{e}_y$, and $\mathbf{e}_z$. Note that $\mathbf{e}_b$, with b running over the same range as a, stands for the same set of e's as $\mathbf{e}_a$ did.

For a reason that will become apparent later, we use an upper index when denoting the components of a vector $\mathbf{V}$ [but more about this later]. Thus we denote the components collectively by V^a, which stands for V^1, V^2, $\ldots$, V^n. Note that, for example, V^2 does not mean "V squared." It means the second component of **V**, and is what we have been calling V_y in three dimensions.

Using the index notation, we can write:

$$\mathbf{V} = \sum_a V^a \mathbf{e}_a, \tag{2.1}$$

where the symbol $\sum_a$ means that we must let a go from 1 to n and must then add the terms that result. For $n = 2$, Equation (2.1) yields essentially Equation (1.1).

The index notation plays an important role in the theory of relativity. Einstein noticed that, when an index letter occurred in an upper position and the same index letter occurred in a lower position in the same term, then almost always a $\sum$ occurred too. So he introduced the *summation convention* according to which an index repeated in this way automatically implies a summation. This removes the unsightly $\sum$'s and makes the work look neater and simpler.

Using the summation convention, we write Equation (2.1) in the form:

$$\mathbf{V} = V^a \mathbf{e}_a, \tag{2.2}$$

which stands for

$$\mathbf{V} = V^1 \mathbf{e}_1 + V^2 \mathbf{e}_2 + \cdots + V^n \mathbf{e}_n.$$

Exercise 2.1 If $V^a = (3, 2)$ and $W_a = (1, 5)$, show that $V^a W_a = 13$.

Exercise 2.2 If $V^b = (1, 3, 6)$ and $W_a = (2, 7, -3)$, show that $V^a W_a = V^b W_b = 5$.

Exercise 2.3 If T^a_b is such that $T^1_1 = 5$, $T^1_2 = -1$, $T^2_1 = 3$, and $T^2_2 = 4$, show that $T^a_a = 9$. What is the value of T^b_b?

Exercise 2.4 How many quantities are there in T^a_b if a and b go from 1 to 3? [*Ans.* 9.] How many if they go from 1 to n?

A linear change from one set of base vectors $\mathbf{e}_a$ to another set $\bar{\mathbf{e}}_a$ with the same origin can be written in the form:

$$\bar{\mathbf{e}}_a = \mathscr{A}^b_a \mathbf{e}_b. \tag{2.3}$$

For example, if a, b have the range 1, 2, and

$$\mathscr{A}^b_a = \begin{array}{c|c|c} {}_a\backslash^b & 1 & 2 \\ \hline 1 & 3 & 4 \\ \hline 2 & 1 & 2 \end{array}, \tag{2.4}$$

then equation (2.3) is essentially the two equations in (1.2); for when $a = 1$ it yields

$$\bar{\mathbf{e}}_1 = \mathscr{A}^b_1 \mathbf{e}_b = \mathscr{A}^1_1 \mathbf{e}_1 + \mathscr{A}^2_1 \mathbf{e}_2 = 3\mathbf{e}_1 + 4\mathbf{e}_2,$$

and similarly for $a = 2$.

Exercise 2.5 Find the values of $\mathscr{A}^b_a$ for Exercises 1.1 and 1.2. [*Ans.*

In Exercise 1.1, $\mathscr{A}_1^1 = 4, \mathscr{A}_1^2 = 1, \mathscr{A}_2^1 = 2, \mathscr{A}_2^2 = 1$.]

Exercise 2.6 Write out Equation (2.3) for the three-dimensional case. [*Ans.* One of the equations is $\bar{\mathbf{e}}_1 = \mathscr{A}_1^1\mathbf{e}_1 + \mathscr{A}_1^2\mathbf{e}_2 + \mathscr{A}_1^3\mathbf{e}_3$.]

When we solve Equation (2.3) for the e's in terms of the ē's, we get an equation of the form,

$$\mathbf{e}_a = A_a^b\bar{\mathbf{e}}_b. \tag{2.5}$$

Thus if a, b have the range 1, 2, and if

$$\mathbf{A}_a^b = \begin{array}{c|c|c} {}_a\backslash^b & 1 & 2 \\ \hline 1 & 1 & -2 \\ \hline 2 & -\frac{1}{2} & \frac{3}{2} \end{array}, \tag{2.6}$$

Equation (2.5) becomes essentially the pair of Equations (1.3).

Exercise 2.7 Write down the values of A_a^b for Exercises 1.1 and 1.2 and save the results for later.

Substituting from Equation (2:5) into Equation (2.2), we have

$$\mathbf{V} = V^a\mathbf{e}_a = V^a(A_a^b\bar{\mathbf{e}}_b) = (A_a^b V^a)\bar{\mathbf{e}}_b. \tag{2.7}$$

But if the components of $\mathbf{V}$ relative to $\bar{\mathbf{e}}_a$ are $\bar{V}^a$ we must have (compare Equation (1.5))

$$\mathbf{V} = \bar{V}^a\bar{\mathbf{e}}_a. \tag{2.8}$$

When we compare this with Equation (2.7) we are puzzled by the fact that $\bar{\mathbf{e}}_b$ appears there but $\bar{\mathbf{e}}_a$ here. But then we remember that we can equally well write Equation (2.8) as

$$\mathbf{V} = \bar{V}^b\bar{\mathbf{e}}_b. \tag{2.9}$$

And comparing this with Equation (2.7) we see that

$$\bar{V}^b = A_a^b V^a. \tag{2.10}$$

This equation means exactly the same thing as do $\bar{V}^a = A_b^a V^b$, $\bar{V}^c = A_a^c V^a$, etc. For the indices that occur on both sides of the equality signs merely label n equations one after the other, while the summed indices indicate the same summation in each case. Indices that are summed according to the summation convention are called *dummy indices*.

Exercise 2.8 In deriving Equation (2.7), we moved parentheses and changed the order of terms in a product. Our experiences with cross products make us wary of such maneuvers. Show, for the two-dimensional case, that $V^a(A_a^b\bar{\mathbf{e}}_b) = (V^a A_a^b)\bar{\mathbf{e}}_b = V^1A_1^1\bar{\mathbf{e}}_1 + V^1A_1^2\bar{\mathbf{e}}_2 + V^2A_2^1\bar{\mathbf{e}}_1 + V^2A_2^2\bar{\mathbf{e}}_2$, and similarly that $V^aA_a^b = A_a^bV^a$. Then extend the results to the n-dimensional case.

From Equations (2.10) and (2.5), we see that $\bar{V}^a$ is given in terms of V^a by means of the same A_b^a that gives $\mathbf{e}_a$ in terms of $\bar{\mathbf{e}}_a$ (not $\bar{\mathbf{e}}_a$ in terms of $\mathbf{e}_a$).

Accordingly **V** is called a *contravariant vector*. Note, though, that in Equation (2.10) the summation is over the lower index of A^b_a while in Equation (2.5) it is over the upper index. It is this that causes the displacement of the numbers noted when we compared Equations (1.3) and (1.6).

How are $\mathscr{A}^b_a$ and A^b_a related? To find out, we introduce an index c having the same range as a and b, and we write Equation (2.5) in the form:

$$\mathbf{e}_b = A^c_b \bar{\mathbf{e}}_c.$$

Applying this to the right-hand side of Equation (2.3) we see that

$$\bar{\mathbf{e}}_a = \mathscr{A}^b_a \mathbf{e}_b = \mathscr{A}^b_a A^c_b \bar{\mathbf{e}}_c. \tag{2.11}$$

For convenience, let us write,

$$\mathscr{A}^b_a A^c_b = \delta^c_a. \tag{2.12}$$

Then Equation (2.11) takes the form:

$$\bar{\mathbf{e}}_a = \delta^c_a \bar{\mathbf{e}}_c. \tag{2.13}$$

Since this is summed over c, we must have

$$\delta^c_a = \begin{cases} 1 \text{ if } a = c \\ 0 \text{ if } a \neq c. \end{cases} \tag{2.14}$$

Because of its importance, this quantity δ^c_a is called the *Kronecker delta*, in honor of a famous mathematician who did not invent it. Equation (2.12), with δ^c_a defined by Equation (2.14), gives us one set of the relations we seek between $\mathscr{A}^b_a$ and A^b_a. It can be written, of course, in the equivalent form:

$$A^c_b \mathscr{A}^b_a = \delta^c_a. \tag{2.15}$$

Exercise 2.9 Why are Equations (2.15) and (2.12) equivalent?

To obtain another relation, we repeat the process in reverse order, applying Equation (2.3) to Equation (2.5). Thus,

$$\mathbf{e}_a = A^b_a \bar{\mathbf{e}}_b = A^b_a \mathscr{A}^c_b \mathbf{e}_c,$$

from which it follows that

$$A^b_a \mathscr{A}^c_b = \delta^c_a. \tag{2.16}$$

While this can be written in the equivalent form

$$\mathscr{A}^c_b A^b_a = \delta^c_a, \tag{2.17}$$

it is not the same as Equations (2.12) and (2.15). Note that the summation is over differently situated indices.

Exercise 2.10 Show that in two dimensions $\delta^a_b = \begin{array}{|c|c|} \hline 1 & 0 \\ \hline 0 & 1 \\ \hline \end{array}$. What is it in n dimensions?

Exercise 2.11 Show that $\delta^b_a T_b = T_b \delta^b_a = T_a$. [*Hint*: $\delta^b_1 T_b = \delta^1_1 T_1 + \delta^2_1 T_2 + \cdots + \delta^n_1 T_n$, and only the first term survives. Similarly, in $\delta^b_2 T_b$ only the second term survives. And so on.]

Exercise 2.12 Show that $\delta^c_a V^a = V^a \delta^c_a = V^c$, and that $\delta^c_a T_{bc} = T_{bc}\delta^c_a = T_{ba}$.

Exercise 2.13 Show that $\delta^a_a = \delta^b_b = n$.

Exercise 2.14 Show that $\delta^a_b T^{bcd}_{ef} = T^{acd}_{ef}$ and note that *the effect of a Kronecker δ is merely to change one index letter on a T to a new letter.*

Exercise 2.15 Using the remark in Exercise 2.14, show that $\delta^a_b \delta^b_c \delta^c_d = \delta^a_d$. What would be the value of $\delta^a_b \delta^b_c \delta^c_d \delta^d_a$?

Working with the base vectors $\mathbf{e}_a$, we found that $\mathscr{A}$ cancels the effect of A, and A cancels the effect of $\mathscr{A}$. Because of this, each is said to be the *inverse* of the other. This cancelling is not confined to the e's. For example, we can easily see that if we solve Equation (2.10) for V^a in terms of $\bar{V}^a$ the result must be:

$$V^a = \mathscr{A}^a_b \bar{V}^b. \tag{2.18}$$

For, using Equation (2.17), we have:

$$\mathscr{A}^a_b \bar{V}^b = \mathscr{A}^a_b A^b_c V^c = \delta^a_c V^c = V^a.$$

Exercise 2.16 Starting with Equation (2.10) and applying Equation (2.18) to the V^a there, show that the A cancels the $\mathscr{A}$, and note that this follows from Equation (2.15), with appropriate indices, rather than from Equation (2.17).

3. THE NEW CONCEPT OF A VECTOR

[In this book we do not consider coordinate systems that are curvilinear or marked off nonuniformly. What follows would need significant modification before it could apply to such systems.]

Take a reference frame with origin O and base vectors $\mathbf{e}_a$. The components of the position vector, $\mathbf{r}$, of a point P are the coordinates of P relative to this frame. In the index notation, we denote the coordinates by x^a, and this lets us write the compact equation:

$$\mathbf{r} = x^a \mathbf{e}_a. \tag{3.1}$$

Equation (2.10) holds for the components of any contravariant vector. Applying it to $\mathbf{r}$, we see that if we go over to a new reference frame having the same origin but different base vectors $\bar{\mathbf{e}}_a$ given, as in Equation (2.3), by

$$\bar{\mathbf{e}}_a = \mathscr{A}^b_a \mathbf{e}_b,$$

the coordinates of P change to $\bar{x}^a$ where

$$\bar{x}^a = A^a_b x^b. \tag{3.2}$$

This suggests a new way of thinking about vectors. We do not harp on arrow-headed line segments. Instead, we say first that a contravariant vector is an entity that has a different set of n components in each coordinate system

—one set per system. And then we add that, if the components are V^a when the coordinates are x^a, and $\bar{V}^a$ when the coordinates are $\bar{x}^a$, and if $\bar{x}^a$ is related to x^a by Equation (3.2), then

$$\bar{V}^a = A^a_b V^b, \tag{3.3}$$

this last being essentially none other than Equation (2.10).

As thus expressed, this is disconcertingly unpictorial, but therein lies its strength, as we shall see. Inasmuch as it deals with components, it embodies an important aspect of the parallelogram law. But for full embodiment, we must add that if, in a particular coordinate system, the components of two vectors are U^a and V^a, then the components of their resultant are $(U^a + V^a)$.

We have now to settle an important question: how do we *know* that we can get away with our statement that a vector, as here regarded, has a *unique* set of components in a given coordinate system? Not simply because we asserted as much: the law of transformation (3.3) might betray us. For example, if we went from coordinates x^a to coordinates $\bar{x}^a$ and from $\bar{x}^a$ to $\hat{x}^a$, the components would go from V^a to $\bar{V}^a$ and then to $\hat{V}^a$. But if we went directly from x^a to $\hat{x}^a$, would the corresponding $\hat{V}^a$ be the same as the previous $\hat{V}^a$? The answer is obviously yes, because V^a transforms exactly as x^a transforms. So the uniqueness of the components in a given coordinate system is assured.

Now comes the crucial theorem: *If U^a and V^a are the components of two contravariant vectors in a given coordinate system, and*

$$U^a = V^a, \tag{3.4}$$

then a corresponding relation holds in all coordinate systems.

This is easily proved. For since

$$\bar{U}^a = A^a_b U^b \quad \text{and} \quad \bar{V}^a = A^a_b V^b, \tag{3.5}$$

we have, by subtraction,

$$\bar{U}_a - \bar{V}_a = A^a_b(U^b - V^b). \tag{3.6}$$

But the right-hand side of Equation (3.6) vanishes, by Equation (3.4), since $U^b - V^b$ is zero for each value of b. So the left-hand side also vanishes and, therefore,

$$\bar{U}^a = \bar{V}^b. \tag{3.7}$$

We now understand how the changeable components can embody objectivity. For if $U^a = V^a$, this equation tells us something that holds for all coordinate systems and, thus, something that is actually independent of the coordinate system used.

Exercise 3.1 By cU^a we mean $(cU^1, cU^2, \ldots, cU^n)$, c being a number. Prove that if U^a are the components of a contravariant vector, cU^a are components of one also. [Simply check that the components of cU^a in any given coordinate system are unique, that they transform according to the law of transformation (3.3), and that they combine correctly with other contravariant vector components. The proofs are extremely easy.]

Exercise 3.2 Let l, m, and n be numbers, and U^a, V^a, and W^a components of contravariant vectors in a given coordinate system. Show that if $lU^a + mV^a - nW^a = 0$, a corresponding relation holds in every coordinate system.

Our new way of looking at vectors suggests new possibilities, for we can think of other ways of attaining uniqueness of components and objectivity. Thus, suppose we have an entity that has components V_a when the coordinates are x^a, and suppose that when we go to new coordinates $\bar{x}^a$ by means of Equation (3.2), the components transform according to the law:

$$\bar{V}_a = \mathscr{A}^{b}_{\bar{a}} V_b. \tag{3.8}$$

Then the components in a given coordinate system are obviously unique, because V_a transforms as the base vectors $\mathbf{e}_a$ do. Also, if U_a and V_a are components of two such entities in the x^a coordinate system, and $U_a = V_a$, then a corresponding relation holds in every other coordinate system. The proof so closely parallels that for $U^a = V^a$ that we shall not bother to write it out.

Clearly, this objective entity with components V_a is entitled to the name vector. It is called a *covariant vector.*

We have only begun, and already we have learned something surprising: there are two types of vectors. Do not make the mistake of thinking that covariant vectors are vectors of a sort that we knew about before, say, pseudovectors. They are not. If we confine ourselves to **ijk** reference frames, including both right-handed and left-handed kinds, it turns out that contravariant and covariant vectors transform in the same way and are thus indistinguishable. But consider, for example, how V^a and V_a behave under the simple change of reference frame $\bar{\mathbf{e}}_a = 12\mathbf{e}_a$. From the laws of transformation, we easily see that $\bar{V}^a = \frac{1}{12}V^a$, but $\bar{V}_a = 12V_a$. [Note that $\mathbf{e}_a$ are contravariant vectors, not convariant vectors. They are printed in boldface type and the index a does not label *their* components.]

Exercise 3.3 In the x^a coordinate system in two dimensions, a contravariant vector and a covariant vector have the same components: $V^a = (3, 5), V_a = (3, 5)$. The coordinates are changed to $\bar{x}^a$ where $\bar{x}^1 = 3x^1 + 2x^2$ and $\bar{x}^2 = x^1 + x^2$. Find $\bar{V}^a$ and $\bar{V}_a$. [*Ans.* $\bar{V}^a = (19, 8)$, $\bar{V}_a = (-2, 9)$. Note that because Equation (2.18) applies to the x's one can obtain $\mathscr{A}^{a}_{\bar{b}}$ by solving for the x's in terms of the $\bar{x}$'s. One finds $\mathscr{A}^1_{\bar{1}} = 1, \mathscr{A}^1_{\bar{2}} = -2, \mathscr{A}^2_{\bar{1}} = -1, \mathscr{A}^2_{\bar{2}} = 3$. Note also that $V^a V_a = \bar{V}^a \bar{V}_a = 34$. This is no accident.]

Exercise 3.4 Like Exercise 3.3 if $V^a = (2, 3)$, $V_a = (2, 3)$, and $\bar{x}^1 = 4x^1 + 5x^2, \bar{x}^2 = 3x^1 + 4x^2$. [*Ans.* $\bar{V}^a = (23, 18)$, $\bar{V}_a = (-1, 2)$. If you mix up the values of $\mathscr{A}^1_{\bar{2}}$ and $\mathscr{A}^2$ you will get the wrong answer $\bar{V}_a = (-7, 6)$. Note that $V^a V_a = \bar{V}^a \bar{V}_a = 13$.]

4. TENSORS

Later we shall tell how to visualize a covariant vector. Meanwhile we find other ideas crowding in on us. For example, if U^a and V^a are components of two contravariant vectors, we can form their various products two at a time, namely U^1V^1, U^1V^2, $U^1V^3, \ldots, U^1V^n$, U^2V^1, $U^2V^2, \ldots$, up to U^nV^n, there being n^2 of them. The index notation lets us represent all n^2 of them by the single symbol U^aV^b. Since U^a and V^a are unique in each coordinate system, the same must be true of U^aV^b, and since U^a and V^a have the objective property, there is a chance that U^aV^b will too. The crucial thing is the way U^aV^b transforms, and we easily see that

$$\bar{U}^a\bar{V}^b = A^a_c A^b_d U^c V^d. \tag{4.1}$$

From this, much as before, we find that if R^a and S^a are also components of contravariant vectors, and $U^aV^b = R^aS^b$, then a corresponding relation holds in every coordinate system.

Exercise 4.1 Prove this.

But now the thought strikes us that we do not need products of vector components in order to have uniqueness and objectivity. We could imagine a a more general entity having n^2 components T^{ab} in the x^a coordinate system, these components transforming as U^aV^b did, namely, according to the law:

$$T^{ab} = A^a_c A^b_d T^{cd}. \tag{4.2}$$

Such an entity will have only one set of components per coordinate system. Also, if two such entities have components S^{ab} and T^{ab} in the x^a coordinate system, and $S^{ab} = T^{ab}$, then a corresponding relation will hold in every coordinate system. For from Equation (4.2) and a similar one for S^{ab} we obtain:

$$\bar{S}^{ab} - \bar{T}^{ab} = A^a_c A^b_d (S^{cd} - T^{cd}).$$

But the n^2 quantities $S^{cd} - T^{cd}$ are all zero. Hence $\bar{S}^{ab} = \bar{T}^{ab}$.

Obviously, an analogous entity with components T_{ab} that transform as the quantities U_aV_b do will have similar objectivity. But why stop here? We can have analogous objective entities with components $T^{ab\cdots}_{cd\cdots}$. All such entities are called *tensors*.

A tensor is an entity having a unique set of components $T^{ab\cdots}_{cd\cdots}$ in a given coordinate system x^a and such that these components transform according to the law:

$$\bar{T}^{ab\cdots}_{cd\cdots} = A^a_r A^b_s \ldots \mathscr{A}^t_c \mathscr{A}^u_d \ldots T^{rs\cdots}_{tu\cdots} \tag{4.3}$$

*when the coordinates are changed as in Equation (3.2).**

Unfortunately we shall have scant opportunity in this book to indicate the

*Strictly speaking. it is incorrect to say that the components in a given coordinate system are unique. If the components are not pure numbers, they will change when the units of length, time, and mass are changed.

crucial role of tensors. Though the above definition is abstract to the point of aridness, tensors are of major importance since they are objective entities. If we wish to represent objective phenomena mathematically, we can hardly escape them.

The tensor law of transformation is easy to remember. For each contravariant index write an A, and for each covariant index an $\mathscr{A}$. Then first put in indices as shown:

$$\bar{T}^{ab\ldots}_{cd\ldots} = A^a A^b \ldots \mathscr{A}_c \mathscr{A}_d \ldots T,$$

and after that, fill in the dummy indices in pairs; note that if, for example, a dummy is placed on $\mathscr{A}_c$, the corresponding dummy goes on T in the position that c occupied on $\bar{T}$.

Exercise 4.2 Cover up Equation (4.3) and write down the laws of transformation for T^b_a, T^a_{bc}, and T^{abc}.

Since it becomes tedious to say "the tensor having components $T^{ab\ldots}_{cd\ldots}$ in a given coordinate system x^a," mathematicians say simply "the tensor $T^{ab\ldots}_{cd\ldots}$," and use similar contractions on other occasions, as in the following exercise.

Exercise 4.3 If S^a_{bc} and T^a_{bc} are tensors [note the language], and $S^a_{bc} = T^a_{bc}$ [again, note the language], prove that a corresponding relation holds in every coordinate system. Also prove that if R^a_{bc}, S^a_{bc}, and T^a_{bc} are tensors, l, m, and n are numbers, and $lR^a_{bc} + mS^a_{bc} - nT^a_{bc} = 0$, a corresponding relation holds in every coordinate system. [The meaning of lR^a_{bc} is reasonably clear.]

Exercise 4.4 Show that the results in Exercise 4.3 would not hold for R^b_{ac}, S^a_{bc}, and T^a_b.

Exercise 4.5 Generalize Exercises 4.3 and 4.4 to the case of tensors having any number of indices.

Exercise 4.6 If S^a_b and T^{cd} are tensors, show that $S^a_b T^{cd}$ is a tensor. [*Hint:* From the laws of transformation of S^a_b and T^{cd} we see at once that $\bar{S}^a_b \bar{T}^{cd} = A^a_r \mathscr{A}^s_b A^c_t A^d_u S^r_s T^{tu}$, and that is practically all there is to it.]

Exercise 4.7 Generalize Exercise 4.6 to the general case of $S^{a\ldots}_{b\ldots}$ and $T^{a\ldots}_{b\ldots}$.

5. SCALARS. CONTRACTION

The number of indices of a tensor is called the *order* of the tensor, and sometimes its *valence*. Thus T^{ab}_c is of order 3. Often we say that such a tensor has contravariant order 2 and covariant order 1, or that it is of the second contravariant order and the first covariant order. Vectors are tensors of order 1. What about tensors of order zero? Since they have no indices we write them as T (or S, or Q, or some other index-free symbol). The corresponding law of transformation, by Equation (4.3), is just

$$\bar{T} = T.$$

Thus, tensors of zero order are scalars, a fact that probably heightens our respect for the concept of a tensor.

If U_a and V^a are vectors, what can we say about $U_a V^a$? By Exercise (4.7) we know that $U_a V^b$ is a second-order tensor; but $U_a V^a$ has a pair of dummy indices and thus, in a sense, no indices: $U_a V^b$ has n^2 components, but $U_a V^a$ has only one. The notation suggests, as did Exercises (3.3) and (3.4), that $U_a V^a$ is a scalar, and we can easily prove it is one. For we may write the laws of transformation of U_a and V^a as $\bar{U}_a = \mathscr{A}^b_a U_b$ and $\bar{V}^a = A^a_c V^c$. Therefore, using Equation (2.17), we have:

$$\bar{U}_a \bar{V}^a = \mathscr{A}^b_a A^a_c U_b V^c = \delta^b_c U_b V^c = U_c V^c = U_a V^a.$$

Exercise 5.1 If T^a_b is a tensor, prove that T^a_a is a scalar.

Exercise 5.2 If T^{ab}_c is a tensor, prove that T^{ab}_a is a contravariant vector.

Exercises 5.1 and 5.2 are special cases of the following general theorem:

If $T^{\cdots a \cdots}_{\cdots b \cdots}$ *is a tensor of order r, then* $T^{\cdots a \cdots}_{\cdots a \cdots}$ *is a tensor of order r — 2.*

We omit the proof. It is the same as that in Exercise 5.1, except for the presence of dots all over the place. The process of summing over a repeated index, one contravariant and the other covariant, to obtain a tensor of lower order is called *contraction.*

The proof that contraction yields a tensor depends crucially on the presence of an $\mathscr{A}$ and an A that combine to form a δ. So, even if an expression like T^{aa} or T_{aa} were summed over a, the result would not be a scalar. We can easily verify this by referring to Exercise (3.3). There $\sum_a V^a V^a = 9 + 25 = 34$, but $\sum_a \bar{V}^a \bar{V}^a = 19^2 + 8^2$ which is too unpleasant to be worth evaluating but is obviously not 34. Also, $\sum_a V_a V_a$ was equal to 34 there too, but $\sum_a \bar{V}_a \bar{V}_a$ comes to 85. There is something disquieting about this, as we shall see later.

6. VISUALIZING TENSORS

The title of this section almost constitutes fraudulent labelling. The fact is that, with a few exceptions, tensors cannot be readily visualized.

Scalars we are familiar with, and therefore, perhaps we feel that we can visualize them. Contravariant vectors we picture as arrow-headed line segments, albeit with a curious mode of combination. But what of covariant vectors?

If V_a is a covariant vector, the quantity $V_a x^a$ is a scalar, since x^a is a contravariant vector. So if we write the equation,

$$V_a x^a = 1, \tag{6.1}$$

it will mean the same thing in all coordinate systems. In two dimensions it is, in the x, y notation, just

$$V_x x + V_y y = 1,$$

which represents a straight line. So we can visualize V_a in two dimensions as this straight line. But do not jump to conclusions. It is not a line *segment*—with or without an arrowhead. It is a whole line. Moreover, in three dimensions Equation (6.1) becomes

$$V_x x + V_y y + V_z z = 1,$$

which represents a plane, not a line. So we can there picture V_a as this plane. For the record we mention, without elaboration, that in n dimensions we can picture V_a as an $(n - 1)$-dimensional hyperplane.

A second-order covariant tensor T_{ab} can be pictured with the aid of the equation:

$$T_{ab} x^a x^b = 1. \tag{6.2}$$

In two dimensions this represents an ellipse, a hyperbola, or a pair of lines.* In three dimesions it represents an ellipsoid, a hyperboloid, a cylinder, or a pair of planes.* As we see, the game of visualization becomes more complicated the greater the number of indices, and we shall pursue it no further except to remark that the above process does not apply to contravariant indices.

Exercise 6.1 In two dimensions if $T_{11} = T_{22} = 1$, $T_{12} = T_{21} = 0$, in rectangular Cartesian coordinates, show that Equation (6.2) represents a circle.

7. SYMMETRY AND ANTISYMMETRY. CROSS PRODUCTS

If a tensor T^{ab} is such that

$$T^{ab} = T^{ba} \tag{7.1}$$

in one coordinate system, a similar relation holds in every coordinate system. For we have

$$\bar{T}^{ab} = A^a_c A^b_d T^{cd} \tag{7.2}$$

$$\bar{T}^{ba} = A^b_c A^a_d T^{cd} \tag{7.3}$$

But in Equation (7.3) we can replace T^{cd} by T^{dc}, because of Equation (7.1). Therefore,

$$\bar{T}^{ba} = A^b_c A^a_d T^{dc}.$$

Since the c's and d's are dummy indices, we can change them to other letters.

*Which may coincide.

So we change both of the present c's to d's and, at the same time, both of the present d's to c's. The result is:

$$\bar{T}^{ba} = A^b_d A^a_c T^{cd},$$

which is identical with

$$\bar{T}^{ba} = A^a_c A^b_d T^{cd}.$$

Comparing this with Equation (7.2) we see that $\bar{T}^{ab} = \bar{T}^{ba}$.

Thus the relation $T^{ab} = T^{ba}$ is an objective one. We say that this T^{ab} is *symmetric* in the indices a and b. In a similar way, one finds that the relationship

$$T^{ab} = -T^{ba} \tag{7.4}$$

is also an objective one. Such a tensor is said to be *antisymmetric*, or *skew symmetric.*

Exercise 7.1 If $T^{ab} = \begin{array}{|c|c|}\hline 1 & 3 \\ \hline 3 & 5 \\ \hline \end{array}$, then $T^{ab} = T^{ba}$. Calculate $\bar{T}^{ab}$ if $\bar{x}^1 = 2x^1 + 4x^2$, $\bar{x}^2 = x^1 + 3x^2$, and verify that $\bar{T}^{ab} = \bar{T}^{ba}$.

Exercise 7.2 If $T^{ab} = \begin{array}{|c|c|}\hline 0 & 3 \\ \hline -3 & 0 \\ \hline \end{array}$, then $T^{ab} = -T^{ba}$. Calculate $\bar{T}^{ab}$ for the coordinate transformation in Exercise 7.1 and verify that $\bar{T}^{ab} = -\bar{T}^{ba}$.

Exercise 7.3 Prove that the relationships $T_{ab} = T_{ba}$ and $T_{ab} = -T_{ba}$ are objective.

Given two vectors U^a and V^a, we can form the second-order antisymmetric tensor:

$$T^{ab} = U^a V^b - U^b V^a. \tag{7.5}$$

Let us write out its components in the three-dimensional case. We easily see that T^{11}, T^{22}, and T^{33} are zero. As for T^{23}, T^{31}, and T^{12}, they are respectively $U^2V^3 - U^3V^2$, $U^3V^1 - U^1V^3$, $U^1V^2 - U^2V^1$; and if we look closely we recognize that THEY ARE OF THE SAME FORM AS THE COMPONENTS OF THE CROSS PRODUCT $\mathbf{U} \times \mathbf{V}$ RELATIVE TO A RIGHT-HAND UNIT ORTHOGONAL TRIAD **i, j, k.** This rouses our interest, and we naturally wonder what the remaining components of T^{ab}, namely T^{32}, T^{13}, and T^{21}, will be. But, since T^{ab} is antisymmetric, they are obviously the negatives of the above—a fact that reminds us of the trouble we had with the changing sign of $\mathbf{U} \times \mathbf{V}$ when we went from a right-handed to a left-handed reference frame.

It can be shown that *if we confine ourselves to right-handed unit orthogonal reference frames* the components T^{23}, T^{31}, and T^{12} transform like the components of a vector (as also do the components T^{32}, T^{13}, and T^{21}). It is this fact that caused our luck to hold when we dealt with cross products as though they were vectors. If you look back you will see that we worked with their components only with respect to **ijk** reference frames. Had we used more general frames we would have encountered difficulties. Indeed, even if we had used base vectors that were not of unit magnitude, though still mutually perpen dicular, we would have encountered trouble—as we realize from the awkwardness connected with $\mathbf{i} \times \mathbf{j} = \mathbf{k}$.

Exercise 7.4 Write out the four components of $U^a V^b - U^b V^a$ for the two-dimensional case, and note that two of them are necessarily zero, and the other two, if they are not zero, are equal except for sign. Show that this holds for any second order antisymmetric tensor T^{ab} or T_{ab} in two dimensions.

Exercise 7.5 Show that in four dimensions a second-order antisymmetric tensor T^{ab} or T_{ab} has four components that are necessarily zero, and twelve components which, if they are not zero, are equal in pairs except for sign.

Exercise 7.6 In two dimensions, if T^{ab} is an antisymmetric tensor it involves, essentially, the single numerical quantity $T^{12} (= -T^{21})$. Show that T^{12} does not transform like a scalar but that

$$\bar{T}^{12} = (A^1_1 A^2_2 - A^1_2 A^2_1) T^{12}.$$

[Use the facts that $T^{11} = T^{22} = 0$; $T^{21} = -T^{12}$.]

In Exercise 7.6, if we restrict ourselves to transformations between right-handed unit orthogonal base vectors, it can be shown that $A^1_1 A^2_2 - A^1_2 A^2_1 = 1$. For such reference frames, then, T^{ab} does behave like a scalar. But if we go from a right-handed frame of this sort to a left-handed one, or vice versa, it changes sign. It is called a *pseudoscalar*.

Usually the components of a tensor change when the coordinates are changed. But consider a tensor T^a_b that has components δ^a_b in the x^a coordinate system. In a new system its components are:

$$\bar{T}^a_b = A^a_c \mathscr{A}^d_b T^c_d = A^a_c \mathscr{A}^d_b \delta^c_d = A^a_c \mathscr{A}^c_b = \delta^a_b,$$

by Equation (2.15). So this particular tensor has the unusual property that its components are the same in every coordinate system. We therefore speak of "the tensor δ^a_b."

Consider a Kronecker delta with two covariant indices:

$$\delta_{ab} = \begin{cases} 1 \text{ if } a = b \\ 0 \text{ if } a \neq b. \end{cases} \tag{7.6}$$

If a tensor T_{ab} has components δ_{ab} in one coordinate system, does it too have the same components in all systems? We have

$$\bar{T}_{ab} = \mathscr{A}^c_a \mathscr{A}^d_b \delta_{cd},$$

but we cannot continue as we did before. The right side does not, in general, reduce to δ_{ab}. So the answer to our question is *no*. Putting it another way, we can say that "δ_{ab} is not a tensor."

Exercise 7.7 Show that "δ^{ab} is not a tensor."

8. MAGNITUDES. THE METRICAL TENSOR

If (V_x, V_y, V_z) are the components of a contravariant vector **V** relative to **i**, **j**, **k**, the square of the magnitude of **V** is given by:

$$(V)^2 = (V_x)^2 + (V_y)^2 + (V_z)^2. \tag{8.1}$$

This fact gave us no qualms when we first encountered it. But now it puzzles us. For we regard $(V)^2$ as a scalar, but the right-hand side of Equation (8.1) is not a scalar. We could express it as $\sum V^a V^a$, but that does not fit the summation convention. So we try $\delta_{ab} V^a V^b$. This *does* fit our notation, and if δ_{ab} were a tensor, this expression would indeed be a scalar, being the double contraction of a tensor. But as we have just seen δ_{ab} is not a tensor.

If we insist on $(V)^2$ being a scalar, we have to say that, though δ_{ab} is not a tensor (in the sense that it does not retain the components δ_{ab} in all coordinate systems) there nevertheless must exist a tensor, say g_{ab}, *that has the components* δ_{ab} *in an* **ijk** *reference frame*:

$$g_{ab} = \delta_{ab}. \tag{8.2}$$

Then we can write Equation (8.1) in the form

$$(V)^2 = g_{ab} V^a V^b, \tag{8.3}$$

with the right-hand side now manifestly a scalar. Since this tensor equation holds in one coordinate system, it holds in all coordinate systems. The tensor g_{ab} is called the *metrical tensor*. As defined, it is obviously symmetric, since $\delta_{ab} = \delta_{ba}$ and symmetry in one reference frame implies symmetry in all. And we note that we can make Equations (8.2) and (8.3) apply to the n-dimensional case by letting a, b have the range $1, 2, \ldots, n$, the coordinates being the analogue of those in an **ijk** frame.

Let us get an idea of the role of the metrical tensor by discussing a simple case. Consider a vector **V** with components V^a relative to **ijk**. Suppose we stretch the x coordinate by the transformation

$$\bar{x}^1 = \alpha x^1, \qquad \bar{x}^2 = x^2, \qquad \bar{x}^3 = x^3. \tag{8.4}$$

Then

$$\bar{V}^1 = \alpha V^1, \qquad \bar{V}^2 = V^2, \qquad \bar{V}^3 = V^3. \tag{8.5}$$

Also, since $x^1 = (1/\alpha)\bar{x}^1$, we have $\mathscr{A}^1_1 = 1/\alpha$, and from the law of transformation,

$$\bar{g}_{ab} = \mathscr{A}^c_a \mathscr{A}^d_b g_{cd},$$

we find after a short calculation that

$$\bar{g}_{11} = \frac{1}{\alpha^2}, \qquad \bar{g}_{ab} = g_{ab} \quad \text{for} \quad b \neq 1. \tag{8.6}$$

Had we taken the sum of the squares of the components $\bar{V}^a$ they would not have given the same result as the sum of the squares of the components V^a. But the g_{ab} acts as a sort of counterpoise to annul the effect of the stretching of the x^1 coordinate, and we have:

$$\bar{g}_{ab}\bar{V}^a\bar{V}^b = \frac{1}{\alpha^2}(\bar{V}^1)^2 + (\bar{V}^2)^2 + (\bar{V}^3)^2$$

$$= \frac{1}{\alpha^2}(\alpha V^1)^2 + (V^2)^2 + (V^3)^2 = (V^1)^2 + (V^2)^2 + (V^3)^2.$$

Exercise 8.1 Apply the transformation $\bar{x}^1 = \alpha x^1$, $\bar{x}^2 = \beta x^2$, $\bar{x}^3 = \gamma x^3$ to the components of g_{ab} in Equation (8.2) and find $\bar{g}_{ab}$. Also find $\bar{V}^a$ in terms of V^a. Then verify that $\bar{g}_{ab}\bar{V}^a\bar{V}^b$ comes to the same thing as $\delta_{ab}V^aV^b$.

Exercise 8.2 In one dimension, if $V^1 = 2$ and $g_{11} = 9$, what is V? [*Ans.* 6.]

Exercise 8.3 If $V^a = (3, -1)$ and $g_{ab} = \begin{array}{|c|c|} \hline 1 & 2 \\ \hline 2 & 6 \\ \hline \end{array}$, show that $V = \sqrt{3}$.

Exercise 8.4 If $V^a = (1, 2, 2, 4)$ and $g_{ab} = \begin{array}{|c|c|c|c|} \hline 5 & 0 & 0 & -1 \\ \hline 0 & 2 & 0 & 0 \\ \hline 0 & 0 & 1 & 0 \\ \hline -1 & 0 & 0 & 1 \\ \hline \end{array}$,

show that $V = 5$.

Exercise 8.5 Given the coordinate transformation $\bar{x}^1 = x^1 + x^2$, $\bar{x}^2 = x^2$, and $\bar{x}^3 = x^3$, solve for the x's in terms of the $\bar{x}$'s and thus obtain $\mathscr{A}^a_b$. Using this, show that the g_{ab} in Equation (8.2) transforms into $\bar{g}_{ab}$ where $\bar{g}_{22} = 2$ and $\bar{g}_{12} = \bar{g}_{21} = -1$, while the other components are unchanged. Then show that $(V)^2 = (\bar{V}^1)^2 + 2(\bar{V}^2)^2 + (\bar{V}^3)^2 - 2\bar{V}^1\bar{V}^2$. [The coefficient -2 in the last term arises from the addition of two terms, one involving $\bar{g}_{12}$ and the other, $\bar{g}_{21}$.]

9. SCALAR PRODUCTS

Given two contravariant vectors U^a and V^a, we can form the scalar $g_{ab}U^aV^b$. What does it represent?

From the analogue of Equation (8.2) in the n-dimensional case, we see that in uniform unit rectangular coordinates,

$$g_{ab}U^aV^b = U^1V^1 + U^2V^2 + \cdots + U^nV^n,$$

which, in the three-dimensional case, is just the scalar product $\mathbf{U}\cdot\mathbf{V}$. Since $g_{ab}U^aV^b$ is a scalar, it has the same value in all coordinate systems. Therefore even when the coordinates are such that terms like $5U^1V^1$ and $3U^1V^2$ appear on the right, it still represents the scalar product. Indeed, we call it the scalar product of $\mathbf{U}$ and $\mathbf{V}$ even in the n-dimensional case.

If we think of **U** and **V** as arrow-headed line segments starting at O, we may write, therefore,

$$g_{ab}U^aV^b = UV\cos\theta, \tag{9.1}$$

where θ is the angle between them. Therefore,

$$\cos\theta = \frac{(g_{ab}U^aV^b)}{\sqrt{g_{cd}U^cU^d}\sqrt{g_{ef}V^eV^f}}. \tag{9.2}$$

This argument is all very well for three dimensions. But isn't it a little reckless for n dimensions?

Not really. One of the nice things about a tensor equation is that we can check its validity by using any convenient coordinate system. So let us take coordinates such that **U** lies along the x^1-axis and has components $U^a = (U^1, 0, 0, \ldots, 0)$, and **V** lies along the x^2-axis and has components $V^a = (0, V^2, 0, \ldots, 0)$. Then Equations (9.1) and (9.2), when expanded, yield the same equations we would get if we worked two-dimensionally in the plane containing **U** and **V**.

Exercise 9.1 Show that $g_{ab}U^aV^b = g_{ab}V^aU^b$. [Use the symmetry of g_{ab}.]

Exercise 9.2 If $U^a = (2, 1)$ and V^a, g_{ab} are as in Exercise 8.3, find $g_{ab}U^aV^b$ and $\cos\theta$. [*Ans.* $2, \sqrt{2}/3\sqrt{3}$.]

Exercise 9.3 If $U^a = (3, 1)$, $V^a = (2, 5)$, and $g_{ab} = \begin{bmatrix} 2 & 1 \\ 1 & 4 \end{bmatrix}$, find U, V, and $\cos\theta$. [*Ans.* $\sqrt{28}, \sqrt{128}, 49/\sqrt{28}\sqrt{128}$.]

Exercise 9.4 If $U^a = (5, 0, 0, 0)$, and V^a and g_{ab} are as in Exercise 8.4, find $g_{ab}U^aV^b$ and $\cos\theta$. [*Ans.* $5, 1/5\sqrt{5}$.]

Exercise 9.5 Show that the angle θ between the x^1- and x^2-axes is given by $\cos\theta = g_{12}/\sqrt{g_{11}g_{22}}$. [Consider $U^a = (U^1, 0, 0, \ldots, 0)$ and $V^a = (0, V^2, 0, \ldots, 0)$.]

Exercise 9.6 Show that if $g_{ab} = 0$ when $a \neq b$, the coordinate axes are mutually perpendicular. [Use the preceding exercise.]

Exercise 9.7 If $U^a = (m, 2)$, and V^a and g_{ab} are as in Exercise 8.3, what must be the value of m if U^a is perpendicular to V^a? [*Ans.* 0.]

Exercise 9.8 Using Exercise 9.5, show that the angle between the $\bar{x}^1$- and $\bar{x}^2$-axes in Exercise 8.5 is 135°. Then see if you can obtain the same result by considering the diagrammatical significance of $\bar{x}^1 = x^1 + x^2$. [The second part is easy once you see it. But there is an enticing false trail that leads to the incorrect answer 45°.]

Exercise 9.9 Show that in Exercise 8.5 the scale on the $\bar{x}^2$-axis is $\sqrt{2}$ times that along the $\bar{x}^1$- and $\bar{x}^3$-axes. [*Hint*: Consider a vector $\bar{V}^a$ with components $(0, 1, 0)$ which thus lies along the $\bar{x}^2$-axis and stretches from the origin to the "1" mark on that axis. Find its magnitude, using the values of $\bar{g}_{ab}$, and compare it with the magnitudes of vectors with components (1, 0, 0) and (0, 0, 1).]

Exercise 9.10 If x^a are coordinates in three dimensions associated with an **ijk** frame, and we define new coordinates by $\bar{x}^1 = x^1 + 2x^2 + x^3$, $\bar{x}^2 = x^2$, $\bar{x}^3 = x^3$, find the cosine of the angle between the $\bar{x}^1$- and $\bar{x}^2$-axes, and the relationship of the scales along these axes. [*Ans.* We find that $\bar{g}_{11} = 1$, $\bar{g}_{22} = 5$, and $\bar{g}_{12} = -2$. So $\cos\theta = -2/\sqrt{5}$, and the ratio of the scales is $\sqrt{5}$.]

Exercise 9.11 What are the components of the metrical tensor in two dimensions when the scale along the x^1-axis is such that the "1" mark on it is 2 inches from the origin, the scale along the x^2-axis is such that the "1" mark on it is $\sqrt{3}$ inches from the origin, and the cosine of the angle between the axes is $\frac{1}{2}$? [*Ans.* $g_{11} = 4$, $g_{22} = 3$, $g_{12} = \sqrt{3}$.]

When we work with **ijk** frames, the metrical tensor has components δ_{ab}. This makes it practically invisible, because we rarely write coefficients that are 1 or 0. When, for example, in the two-dimensional case we write

$$(V)^2 = (V^1)^2 + (V^2)^2,$$

we are not likely to realize that this is really

$$(V)^2 = 1V^1V^1 + 0V^1V^2 + 0V^2V^1 + 1V^2V^2 = \delta_{ab}V^aV^b = g_{ab}V^aV^b.$$

Since the components of a displacement are pure numbers but its magnitude is a length, we see that the components of the metrical tensor must have the dimensions of the square of a length. And this brings us to something that may have been worrying you for quite a while. When we complained about $\mathbf{i} \times \mathbf{j} = \mathbf{k}$, should we not also have complained about $\mathbf{i} \cdot \mathbf{i} = 1$? That equation, too, is unsatisfactory, since the left-hand side is the square of a length, but the right hand side looks like a pure number.

With the aid of the metrical tensor, we can clarify the situation. The vector **i** has components (1, 0, 0) relative to the **ijk** frame; the 1 is a pure number, not a length. Denote these components of **i** by i^a. Then,

$$\mathbf{i} \cdot \mathbf{i} = g_{ab}i^a i^b = g_{11}i^1 i^1 = g_{11},$$

and though g_{11} here has the value 1, the right-hand side is now explicitly the square of a length, as it has to be.

Exercise 9.12 A vector V^a lies along the x^1-axis and has components $(V^1, 0, 0, \ldots, 0)$. Show that its magnitude is not V^1 but $\sqrt{g_{11}}\, V^1$.

10. WHAT THEN IS A VECTOR?

This being a book about vectors, we have presented only the sketchiest account of tensors—barely enough to illustrate the advantages of thinking of vectors in terms of the way their components transform.

We have one final point to make. Notice that we defined contravariant vectors and covariant vectors—indeed, tensors of all ranks—*before we introduced the metrical tensor*. Suppose there were no metrical tensor. What could we then say about the magnitudes of vectors? Or about the cosines of the angles between them?

You may be tempted to argue that such questions prove that there *has* to be a metrical tensor. But actually there does not. Mathematicians often work with spaces that do not possess one; they call them *nonmetrical spaces.*

Thus vectors do not *have* to have magnitudes. And this is as good a place as any to stop.

INDEX